HEATH CHEMISTRY

COMPUTER TEST BANK

Teacher's Guide

D. C. HEATH AND COMPANY
Lexington, Massachusetts / Toronto, Ontario

The Heath Chemistry Program

Heath Chemistry, Pupil's Edition
Heath Chemistry, Teacher's Annotated Edition
Heath Chemistry Laboratory Experiments,
  Pupil's Edition
Heath Chemistry Laboratory Experiments,
  Teacher's Annotated Edition
Heath Chemistry Chapter Worksheets
Heath Chemistry Teacher's Resource Binder
Heath Chemistry Tests, Spirit Duplicating Masters
Heath Chemistry Computer Test Bank
Heath Chemistry Computer Test Bank, Teacher's Guide
Heath Chemistry Courseware
Heath Chemistry Lab Assistant

Editorial Development: Navta Associates, Inc.
Cover Photograph: Richard Megna/Fundamental Photos

Published simultaneously in Canada
Printed in the United States of America
International Standard Book Number: 0-669-12877-5

CONTENTS

How to Use the *Heath Chemistry Computer Test Bank*

The *Heath Chemistry Computer Test Bank* has been designed to assist you in constructing tests based on content presented in *Heath Chemistry.* The test bank and its computer software, the use of which is explained in a separate manual, allow you to produce quizzes and chapter, unit, midyear, and end-of-year tests. This Teacher's Guide, which is a printed copy of the test items contained on three microcomputer disks, allows you to see all chapter items at a glance. It can be used either independently or in conjunction with the software. The software, entitled *Archive II,* is an item banking, test construction, and test printing system.

The test items cover each chapter of *Heath Chemistry* emphasizing all major concepts contained in the chapter. Each chapter has approximately 60 items that are organized by format and comprehension level. The formats are true/false (T), open-ended (O), and multiple-choice (M), respectively. The two taxonomic levels of comprehension are *recall* and *inferential. Recall* questions test student ability to recall facts and definitions presented in the text. *Inferential* items require students to interpret questions in light of information presented in the chapters. Approximately 60 percent of the items are written at the recall level. Approximately 40 percent of the items test students at the inferential level. (The percentage of inferential questions includes the test items for the laboratory experiments.) Each item in the bank is labeled *1* (recall) or *2* (inferential) to identify the taxonomic level.

In addition to taxonomic levels *1* and *2,* you will find two other levels by which questions may be sorted. Level *3* items test concepts presented in the *Extension* and/or the *Application* sections of the text chapters, which may be considered optional portions of otherwise essential material. The level *3* category gives you the option to omit or include these test items at your discretion. Level *4* items test student knowledge and application skills as related to the *Heath Chemistry Laboratory Experiments.* With this selection option, you can create tests that cover only the laboratory work, or you may integrate lab test items into your chapter tests.

With this background, you are ready to construct tests using the item banking and test construction capabilities of *Archive II.* The software presents teachers with several testing options. Test items can be sorted by chapter, by sections within a chapter, by question type, or by taxonomic level. Consult the *Archive II* user's manual to learn the various test-construction options.

Once a test has been constructed, a printer attached to the microcomputer can be used to produce a master copy of the test as well as an answer key. Adjacent to each test item is a text reference that indicates the section where relevant material appears in a chapter. This information can be used during test construction or to provide follow-up instruction. Correct responses for true/false and multiple-choice items appear in answer keys as well as in this Teacher's Guide. For open-ended items requiring a one-word or two-word answer, the best answer appears in the answer key.

Below is an example of an individual item as it appears in the Teacher's Guide. The format identifies an item's sequential number within a chapter, type (T, O, or M), taxonomic level (1, 2, 3, or 4), text reference (section number), and correct response. The corresponding test item is also shown as it appears on the student's test.

Teacher's Guide

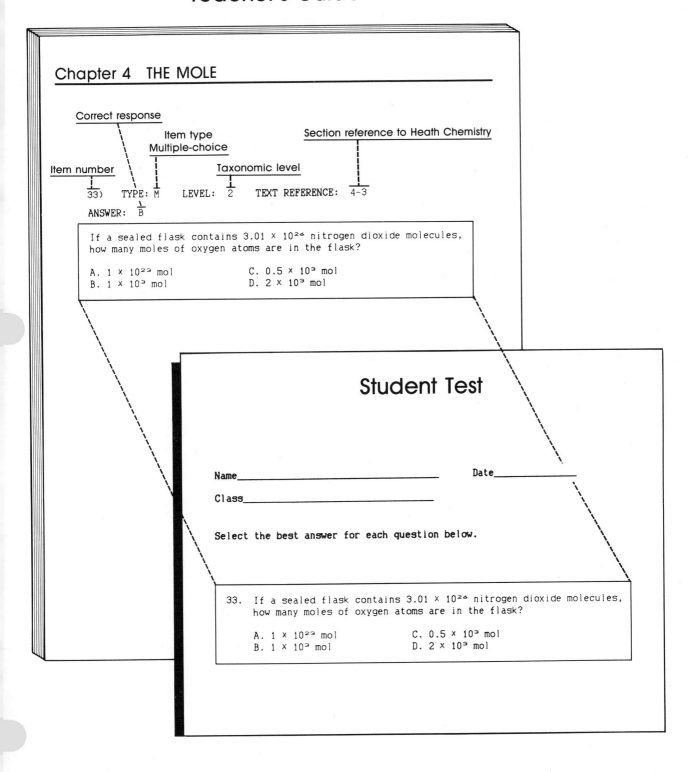

Chapter 4 THE MOLE

Correct response

Item type
Multiple-choice

Section reference to Heath Chemistry

Item number

Taxonomic level

33) TYPE: M LEVEL: 2 TEXT REFERENCE: 4-3

ANSWER: B

If a sealed flask contains 3.01×10^{24} nitrogen dioxide molecules, how many moles of oxygen atoms are in the flask?

A. 1×10^{23} mol C. 0.5×10^3 mol
B. 1×10^3 mol D. 2×10^3 mol

Student Test

Name_____ Date_____

Class_____

Select the best answer for each question below.

33. If a sealed flask contains 3.01×10^{24} nitrogen dioxide molecules, how many moles of oxygen atoms are in the flask?

A. 1×10^{23} mol C. 0.5×10^3 mol
B. 1×10^3 mol D. 2×10^3 mol

Chapter 1   ACTIVITIES OF SCIENCE

1) TYPE: T   LEVEL: 2   TEXT REFERENCE: 1-1
ANSWER: T

_____   Communications between scientists about their experiments and
        observations increases the amount of knowledge we accept as
        fact.

2) TYPE: T   LEVEL: 1   TEXT REFERENCE: 1-1
ANSWER: T

_____   Most people who observe the same thing will have different
        inferences.

3) TYPE: T   LEVEL: 1   TEXT REFERENCE: 1-2
ANSWER: F

_____   A model is always a physical object.

4) TYPE: T   LEVEL: 1   TEXT REFERENCE: 1-3
ANSWER: F

_____   All matter has mass but not necessarily inertia.

5) TYPE: T   LEVEL: 1   TEXT REFERENCE: 1-5
ANSWER: T

_____   Most matter, even iron or stone, can exist in any of the
        three common physical states known as solid, liquid, or gas.

6) TYPE: T   LEVEL: 1   TEXT REFERENCE: 1-6
ANSWER: T

_____   During an energy conversion such as burning coal to produce
        heat there is no actual loss or gain of energy.

7) TYPE: T   LEVEL: 1   TEXT REFERENCE: 1-7
ANSWER: F

_____   A cubit is a standard measurement used by most scientists.

8) TYPE: T   LEVEL: 1   TEXT REFERENCE: 1-8
ANSWER: F

_____   The only way to describe quantities is by using SI units.

9) TYPE: T   LEVEL: 2   TEXT REFERENCE: 1-10
ANSWER: T

_____   It is important to include units in your equations to check
        the logic used to solve the problems.

10) TYPE: T   LEVEL: 1   TEXT REFERENCE: 1-10
ANSWER: T

_____   The rules of mathematics which apply to numbers also apply to
        units.

11) TYPE: T   LEVEL: 1   TEXT REFERENCE: 1-11
ANSWER: T

_____   Size is described by derived units such as area or volume.

12) TYPE: T   LEVEL: 1   TEXT REFERENCE: 1-12
ANSWER: T

_____   It is always possible to express derived SI units in terms of
        base units.

13) TYPE: T   LEVEL: 2   TEXT REFERENCE: 1-12
ANSWER: T

_____   Positive identification of a substance occurs if it has
        characteristics which match a known substance.

14) TYPE: T   LEVEL: 1   TEXT REFERENCE: 1-12
ANSWER: T

_____   Many times trial and error is used to make new discoveries.

15) TYPE: O   LEVEL: 1   TEXT REFERENCE: 1-1
ANSWER: observation

Science is a way of gaining knowledge based on careful

_____.

16) TYPE: O   LEVEL: 1   TEXT REFERENCE: 1-1
ANSWER: inference

A(n) _____ is an interpretation of an observation.

17) **TYPE:** O   **LEVEL:** 1   **TEXT REFERENCE:** 1-2
ANSWER: regularity

A(n) _____ is a characteristic used to place things into categories.

18) **TYPE:** O   **LEVEL:** 1   **TEXT REFERENCE:** 1-2
ANSWER: classification

The process of categorizing similar things is called _____.

19) **TYPE:** O   **LEVEL:** 1   **TEXT REFERENCE:** 1-2
ANSWER: theory

A(n) _____ is an explanation which accounts for past events and accurately predicts future events.

20) **TYPE:** O   **LEVEL:** 1   **TEXT REFERENCE:** 1-3
ANSWER: matter

Anything that has mass and takes up space is defined as _____.

21) **TYPE:** O   **LEVEL:** 1   **TEXT REFERENCE:** 1-3
ANSWER: inertia

The resistance needed to move, stop, or redirect an object is called _____.

22) **TYPE:** O   **LEVEL:** 1   **TEXT REFERENCE:** 1-4
ANSWER: conserved

It is a general law of nature that matter is _____ when it is changed from one form to another.

23) **TYPE:** O   **LEVEL:** 1   **TEXT REFERENCE:** 1-5
ANSWER: plasma

A(n) _____ is a fourth state of matter similar to a gas.

24) **TYPE:** O   **LEVEL:** 1   **TEXT REFERENCE:** 1-6
ANSWER: energy

Anything that is not matter and can cause a change in matter is _____.

25) **TYPE:** O   **LEVEL:** 1   **TEXT REFERENCE:** 1-6
ANSWER: kinetic

The energy of motion is _____ energy.

26) **TYPE:** O   **LEVEL:** 1   **TEXT REFERENCE:** 1-7
ANSWER: quantity

A(n) _____ is a measureable property that must be described by both a number and a unit.

27) **TYPE:** O   **LEVEL:** 1   **TEXT REFERENCE:** 1-8
ANSWER: SI

Le System International d'unites is abbreviated as _____, and is the worldwide system of measurement.

28) **TYPE:** O   **LEVEL:** 1   **TEXT REFERENCE:** 1-8
ANSWER: temperature

The quantity measured by the SI unit kelvin is _____.

29) **TYPE:** O   **LEVEL:** 1   **TEXT REFERENCE:** 1-8
ANSWER: centi

The metric prefix which means one-tenth is _____.

30) **TYPE:** O   **LEVEL:** 3   **TEXT REFERENCE:** 1-9
ANSWER: indirect

Determination of water hardness is an example of _____ measurement.

31) **TYPE:** O   **LEVEL:** 1   **TEXT REFERENCE:** 1-10
ANSWER: unitary

A conversion ratio whose denominator is one is called a(n) _____ rate.

32) **TYPE:** O   **LEVEL:** 1   **TEXT REFERENCE:** 1-11
ANSWER: area

The number of square units needed to cover a surface describes _____.

33) TYPE: M   LEVEL: 2   TEXT REFERENCE: 1-1
ANSWER: D

Which of the following statements is not an observation?

A. My cat has soft fur.
B. Jim's cat has sharp claws.
C. My cat's eyes are gray.
D. Jim's cat is not as pretty as mine.

34) TYPE: M   LEVEL: 1   TEXT REFERENCE: 1-2
ANSWER: C

"Counting sheep will help you to fall asleep quickly" is a(n):

A. observation.   C. theory.
B. inference.   D. test.

35) TYPE: M   LEVEL: 2   TEXT REFERENCE: 1-3
ANSWER: C

If an object is heavy it will have relatively:

A. little mass.
B. more mass, little inertia.
C. more mass, more inertia.
D. little inertia.

36) TYPE: M   LEVEL: 2   TEXT REFERENCE: 1-4
ANSWER: C

In a closed container, the mass of matter collected after burning as
compared to before burning should be:

A. less.   C. the same.
B. more.   D. can't tell.

37) TYPE: M   LEVEL: 2   TEXT REFERENCE: 1-5
ANSWER: A

Which of the following describes the state of matter for frozen
water?

A. solid   C. gas
B. liquid   D. plasma

38) TYPE: M   LEVEL: 2   TEXT REFERENCE: 1-6
ANSWER: D

An exploding firecracker has:

A. only potential energy.
B. more kinetic energy than potential energy.
C. more potential energy than kinetic energy.
D. only kinetic energy.

39) TYPE: M   LEVEL: 1   TEXT REFERENCE: 1-7
ANSWER: B

In order for quantities to be added or subtracted, they must have the same:

A. mass.   C. volume.
B. unit.   D. unitary rate.

40) TYPE: M   LEVEL: 2   TEXT REFERENCE: 1-7
ANSWER: C

Which of the following is not a quantity?

A. four meters   C. seven
B. 3 wigglesnogs   D. 778 grams

41) TYPE: M   LEVEL: 1   TEXT REFERENCE: 1-8
ANSWER: B

These are all SI units except:

A. kelvin.   C. kilogram.
B. inch.   D. second.

42) TYPE: M   LEVEL: 2   TEXT REFERENCE: 1-8
ANSWER: B

What is your height in centimeters tall is you are 0.01 km tall?

A. 100.0   C. 0.001
B. 1000.0   D. 0.000 01

43) TYPE: M   LEVEL: 2   TEXT REFERENCE: 1-8
ANSWER: D

Which of the following quantities is not expressed in SI units?

A. 10 dm   C. 345 Mm
B. 1 kmol   D. 60 mft

44) TYPE: M   LEVEL: 1   TEXT REFERENCE: 1-8
ANSWER: C

The number of fundamental SI base units that can be used to express
any quantity is:

A. four.   C. seven.
B. six.   D. nine.

45) TYPE: M   LEVEL: 1   TEXT REFERENCE: 1-10
ANSWER: A

"10 mph" is not an example of a(n):

A. SI base unit.   C. conversion quantity.
B. unitary quantity.   D. unitary rate.

46) TYPE: M   LEVEL: 1   TEXT REFERENCE: 1-10
ANSWER: B

Sue has $1.50 to buy candy bars priced at 3/$1.00. Use a ratio to
find how many bars she may buy.

A. 3   C. 5
B. 4   D. 6

47) TYPE: M   LEVEL: 2   TEXT REFERENCE: 1-10
ANSWER: D

It takes two and one-half wigglesnogs to make one bleeker. How many
wigglesnogs must be used to produce four bleekers?

A. four   C. one-hundred
B. one and one-half   D. ten

48) TYPE: M   LEVEL: 1   TEXT REFERENCE: 1-11
ANSWER: B

The SI derived unit m^3 describes:

A. area.   C. speed.
B. volume.   D. length.

49) TYPE: M   LEVEL: 2   TEXT REFERENCE: 1-11
ANSWER: A

How many cubic centimeters are in one cubic meter?

A. 0.000 001   C. 100
B. 0.001   D. 1 000 000

50) TYPE: O   LEVEL: 4   TEXT REFERENCE: LB
ANSWER: chemical

If two liquids are mixed and a gas is formed, a _____
change has taken place.

51) TYPE: O   LEVEL: 4   TEXT REFERENCE: LC
ANSWER: volume

The graduated cylinder may be used to measure _____,
a derived quantity.

52) TYPE: O   LEVEL: 4   TEXT REFERENCE: LC
ANSWER: systematic

An error that causes all of the results in an experiment to differ
from the expected value would be a(n) _____
error.

53) TYPE: O   LEVEL: 4   TEXT REFERENCE: LC
ANSWER: accepted

The _____ value for the mass of one milliliter of
water is one gram.

54) TYPE: M   LEVEL: 4   TEXT REFERENCE: LA
ANSWER: B

Carbon dioxide is produced in a reaction between hydrochloric acid
and:

A. calcium hydroxide.   C. magnesium.
B. sodium carbonate.   D. glycerin.

55) TYPE: M   LEVEL: 4   TEXT REFERENCE: LA
ANSWER: B

A reaction between hydrochloric acid and magnesium is:

A. endothermic.   C. exothermic.
B. neither A nor B.   D. both A and B.

56) TYPE: M   LEVEL: 4   TEXT REFERENCE: LB
ANSWER: D

Which of the following is a chemical change?

A. making ice cubes   C. boiling water
B. an icicle forming   D. burning paper

57) TYPE: M   LEVEL: 4   TEXT REFERENCE: LC
ANSWER: D

Which of the following would not cause systematic errors in
determining the mass of a liquid in a graduated cylinder?

A. The experiment was not done at sea level.   .
B. It is hot in the room.
C. It is very dry in the room.
D. The balances are off.

58) TYPE: M   LEVEL: 4   TEXT REFERENCE: LC
ANSWER: A

A random error in an experiment in which the accepted value of 1.00
would give:

A. as many values greater than 1.00 as less than 1.00.
B. many values greater than 1.00 and a few less than 1.00.
C. many values less than 1.00 and a few greater than 1.00.
D. all of the results either greater than or less than 1.00.

59) TYPE: M   LEVEL: 4   TEXT REFERENCE: LC
ANSWER: B

Which of the following would cause a low value for the density of
water in the beaker?

A. a humid room
B. a small amount of water was left in the beaker
C. using salt water
D. cooling the water

60) TYPE: M   LEVEL: 4   TEXT REFERENCE: LC
ANSWER: D

The units that are generally used to describe the density of water
are:

A. grams.   C. grams per liter.
B. milliliters.   D. grams per milliliter.

1) TYPE: T   LEVEL: 1   TEXT REFERENCE: 2-3
ANSWER: F

_____ The boiling point of a pure substance is the same as its melting point.

2) TYPE: T   LEVEL: 1   TEXT REFERENCE: 2-4
ANSWER: T

_____ Decomposition is a chemical change.

3) TYPE: T   LEVEL: 2   TEXT REFERENCE: 2-4
ANSWER: F

_____ Melting wax is an example of a chemical change.

4) TYPE: T   LEVEL: 1   TEXT REFERENCE: 2-5
ANSWER: T

_____ Distillation is a physical change.

5) TYPE: T   LEVEL: 1   TEXT REFERENCE: 2-6
ANSWER: T

_____ Water is a compound composed of hydrogen and oxygen.

6) TYPE: T   LEVEL: 2   TEXT REFERENCE: 2-6
ANSWER: T

_____ It is possible to make different compounds, each with a definite composition, using the same elements.

7) TYPE: T   LEVEL: 1   TEXT REFERENCE: 2-8
ANSWER: T

_____ An element contains only one kind of atom.

8) TYPE: T   LEVEL: 1   TEXT REFERENCE: 2-8
ANSWER: F

_____ Every element has the same atomic number.

9) TYPE: T   LEVEL: 2   TEXT REFERENCE: 2-8
ANSWER: F

_____ All elements have the same melting and boiling points.

10) TYPE: T   LEVEL: 1   TEXT REFERENCE: 2-12
ANSWER: T

____   A water molecule contains two hydrogen atoms.

11) TYPE: T   LEVEL: 2   TEXT REFERENCE: 2-13
ANSWER: T

____   An ion with a charge of 1+ was probably formed from an
          element in Group 1 of the periodic table.

12) TYPE: T   LEVEL: 1   TEXT REFERENCE: 2-15
ANSWER: F

____   The algebraic sum of all charges in a compound that contains
          polyatomic ions is always 1-.

13) TYPE: T   LEVEL: 2   TEXT REFERENCE: 2-16
ANSWER: F

____   The name of a compound can always be determined from its
          formula.

14) TYPE: O   LEVEL: 1   TEXT REFERENCE: 2-1
ANSWER: freezing

The temperature at which matter changes from a liquid to a solid is
called its _____ point.

15) TYPE: O   LEVEL: 1   TEXT REFERENCE: 2-2
ANSWER: distillation

A procedure used to separate solutions into their component parts is
called _____.

16) TYPE: O   LEVEL: 1   TEXT REFERENCE: 2-2
ANSWER: pure

Matter that is not easily separated into parts is called a(n)
_____ substance.

17) TYPE: O   LEVEL: 1   TEXT REFERENCE: 2-2
ANSWER: solutions

Mixtures that do not scatter light and look the same throughout are
called _____.

18) TYPE: O   LEVEL: 1   TEXT REFERENCE: 2-4
ANSWER: melting

The change of a solid to a liquid without the formation of new matter
is called _____.

19) TYPE: O   LEVEL: 1   TEXT REFERENCE: 2-4
ANSWER: decomposition

A chemical change in which one kind of matter separates to form two
or more distinctly different kinds of matter is called

_____.

20) TYPE: O   LEVEL: 1   TEXT REFERENCE: 2-5
ANSWER: elements

Pure substances that cannot be decomposed are known as

_____.

21) TYPE: O   LEVEL: 1   TEXT REFERENCE: 2-7
ANSWER: macroscopic

An observation made by seeing, feeling, or smelling something is
called a(n) _____ observation.

22) TYPE: O   LEVEL: 1   TEXT REFERENCE: 2-7
ANSWER: macroscopic

Properties of large chunks of matter are called _____
properties.

23) TYPE: O   LEVEL: 1   TEXT REFERENCE: 2-8
ANSWER: molecules

Particles made of more than one atom are called

_____.

24) TYPE: O   LEVEL: 1   TEXT REFERENCE: 2-9
ANSWER: ions

Particles that have an electrical charge are called _____.

25) TYPE: O   LEVEL: 1   TEXT REFERENCE: 2-10
ANSWER: symbols

Chemical _____ are abbreviations for the names of
elements.

26) TYPE: 0   LEVEL: 1   TEXT REFERENCE: 2-12
ANSWER: subscript

In a chemical formula, the _____ indicates the
number of atoms of an element in the compound.

27) TYPE: 0   LEVEL: 1   TEXT REFERENCE: 2-13
ANSWER: binary

Compounds containing two elements are called _____
compounds.

28) TYPE: 0   LEVEL: 2   TEXT REFERENCE: 2-14
ANSWER: two

In a compound made up of barium (charge is 2+) and iodine (charge is
1-) there will always be _____ iodine atoms for every
one atom of barium.

29) TYPE: 0   LEVEL: 1   TEXT REFERENCE: 2-15
ANSWER: polyatomic

Several atoms joined together with a total charge of 1- form what is
called a(n) _____ ion.

30) TYPE: 0   LEVEL: 2   TEXT REFERENCE: 2-15
ANSWER: $Mg(OH)_2$

The formula for a compound containing magnesium ions and hydroxide
ions is _____.

31) TYPE: 0   LEVEL: 1   TEXT REFERENCE: 2-16
ANSWER: dihydrogen monoxide

The common name for H_2O is water, while its systematic name is
_____.

32) TYPE: 0   LEVEL: 2   TEXT REFERENCE: 2-17
ANSWER: oxide

The name for K_2O is potassium _____.

33) TYPE: 0   LEVEL: 1   TEXT REFERENCE: 2-19
ANSWER: tetra-

The Greek prefix for the number four is _____.

34) TYPE: 0 LEVEL: 2 TEXT REFERENCE: 2-19
ANSWER: tetraoxide

The name for P_2O_4 is diphosphorus _____ .

35) TYPE: M LEVEL: 1 TEXT REFERENCE: 2-1
ANSWER: A

The temperature at which matter changes from a liquid to a gas is
the:

A. boiling point.   C. freezing point.
B. melting point.   D. equilibrium point.

36) TYPE: M LEVEL: 1 TEXT REFERENCE: 2-3
ANSWER: A

The melting point of matter is the same as its:

A. freezing point.   C. boiling point.
B. plasma point.   D. distillation point.

37) TYPE: M LEVEL: 2 TEXT REFERENCE: 2-4
ANSWER: B

Melting moth flakes is an example of:

A. chemical change.   C. decomposition.
B. physical change.   D. electrolysis.

38) TYPE: M LEVEL: 2 TEXT REFERENCE: 2-4
ANSWER: C

Which of the following is not an example of a physical change?

A. boiling water   C. melting sugar
B. freezing orange juice   D. boiling ocean water

39) TYPE: M LEVEL: 1 TEXT REFERENCE: 2-5
ANSWER: C

Electrolysis causes matter to:

A. melt.   C. decompose.
B. boil.   D. distill.

40) TYPE: M   LEVEL: 1   TEXT REFERENCE: 2-5
ANSWER: B

99% of the Earth's crust is composed of:

A. twelve elements.   C. fifty-two elements.
B. eight elements.   D. one hundred elements.

41) TYPE: M   LEVEL: 1   TEXT REFERENCE: 2-5
ANSWER: B

Pure substances that can be decomposed into simpler substances are
called:

A. elements.   C. mixtures.
B. compounds.   D. solutions.

42) TYPE: M   LEVEL: 1   TEXT REFERENCE: 2-6
ANSWER: C

The fact that mixtures can have any composition, while compounds have
a definite composition, is called the:

A. law of definite proportion.
B. law of multiple proportions.
C. law of definite composition.
D. law of multiple compositions.

43) TYPE: M   LEVEL: 1   TEXT REFERENCE: 2-8
ANSWER: B

Atoms in a liquid are:

A. farther apart than in a gas.
B. farther apart than in a solid.
C. closer together than in a solid.
D. not any different than in a solid.

44) TYPE: M   LEVEL: 2   TEXT REFERENCE: 2-9
ANSWER: D

What words would you use to describe matter made of three kinds of
atoms that fit very closely together?

A. solid gaseous   C. gaseous element
B. gaseous compound   D. solid compound

45) TYPE: M   LEVEL: 2   TEXT REFERENCE: 2-11
ANSWER: D

Which of the following is not a characteristic of a metal?

A. can be bent
B. high melting point
C. reflects light when polished
D. poor conductor of heat

46) TYPE: M   LEVEL: 1   TEXT REFERENCE: 2-12
ANSWER: A

A chemical formula would not contain:

A. names of compounds.
B. abbreviations for names of elements.
C. symbols of elements.
D. subscripts.

47) TYPE: M   LEVEL: 1   TEXT REFERENCE: 2-13
ANSWER: C

The algebraic sum of the charges in a compound is:

A. always positive.   C. equal to zero.
B. always negative.   D. equal to one.

48) TYPE: M   LEVEL: 2   TEXT REFERENCE: 2-14
ANSWER: D

What is the formula for the compound formed from calcium and oxygen?

A. OCa   C. ClO
B. CA_2O_2 D. CaO

49) TYPE: M   LEVEL: 2   TEXT REFERENCE: 2-17
ANSWER: B

What is the name for NaCl?

A. sodium chlorate   C. potassium chloride
B. sodium chloride   D. neon chlorate

50) TYPE: M   LEVEL: 1   TEXT REFERENCE: 2-11
ANSWER: C

The periodic table gives all of the following information about an
element except:

A. atomic mass.   C. color.
B. symbol.   D. atomic number

51) TYPE: M   LEVEL: 2   TEXT REFERENCE: 2-18
ANSWER: C

What is the charge on nitrogen in NH_3?

A. 1-   C. 3-
B. 1+   D. 3+

52) TYPE: M   LEVEL: 2   TEXT REFERENCE: 2-19
ANSWER: D

What is the name for N_2Cl_3?

A. dinitride tetrachlorine
B. trinitrogen dichloride
C. dinitrogen trichlorine
D. dinitrogen trichloride

53) TYPE: O   LEVEL: 4   TEXT REFERENCE: LC
ANSWER: best estimate/estimated uncertainty

The exact value for a measurement can be assumed to lie within a
range expressed by the _____ and
_____.

54) TYPE: O   LEVEL: 4   TEXT REFERENCE: LC
ANSWER: quantitative

Experiments that include measurements of how much matter is present
or changed are called _____ experiments.

55) TYPE: M   LEVEL: 4   TEXT REFERENCE: LA
ANSWER: A

After ten minutes a reaction between iron filings and methanol
produces:

A. no reaction.   C. rust.
B. bubbles.   D. white crystal.

56) TYPE: M   LEVEL: 4   TEXT REFERENCE: LA
ANSWER: D

A white powder that bubbles after ten minutes in water could be
identified as:

A. sodium chloride.   C. iron filings.
B. sucrose.   D. sodium bicarbonate.

57) TYPE: M   LEVEL: 4   TEXT REFERENCE: LA
ANSWER: D

Which of the following is a sign of a physical change?

A. formation of a gas
B. color change
C. formation of a precipitate
D. none of the above

58) TYPE: M   LEVEL: 4   TEXT REFERENCE: LB
ANSWER: C

How much hydrogen is needed to completely react with 160 g of oxygen?

A. 10 g   C. 20 g
B. 2 g   D. 80 g

59) TYPE: M   LEVEL: 4   TEXT REFERENCE: LB
ANSWER: C

The compound H_2O is a chemical combination of hydrogen and oxygen
in a mass ratio of:

A. 1:2.   C. 1:8.
B. 2:1.   D. 8:1.

60) TYPE: M   LEVEL: 4   TEXT REFERENCE: LB
ANSWER: B

If a 1:4 mole ratio of hydrogen and oxygen are reacted to form water,
there will be:

A. unreacted hydrogen.
B. unreacted oxygen.
C. both A and B.
D. neither A nor B.

61) TYPE: M   LEVEL: 4   TEXT REFERENCE: LC
ANSWER: D

What is the range represented by 42.36 ± 0.03 g?

A. 42.36 to 42.39   C. 42.06 to 42.66
B. 42.36 to 42.33   D. 42.33 to 42.39

1) TYPE: T   LEVEL: 1   TEXT REFERENCE: 3-1
ANSWER: T

____   The quotient of two proportional numbers is a constant.

2) TYPE: T   LEVEL: 1   TEXT REFERENCE: 3-2
ANSWER: T

____   The exponent indicates the number of times the base is
multiplied by itself to give the product.

3) TYPE: T   LEVEL: 1   TEXT REFERENCE: 3-3
ANSWER: F

____   The product of two powers of ten is obtained by subtracting
the exponents.

4) TYPE: T   LEVEL: 1   TEXT REFERENCE: 3-4
ANSWER: T

____   The exponents of numbers to be added or subtracted must be
the same.

5) TYPE: T   LEVEL: 1   TEXT REFERENCE: 3-7
ANSWER: T

____   The most common reason for uncertainty in measurement is that
instruments are limited.

6) TYPE: T   LEVEL: 2   TEXT REFERENCE: 3-8
ANSWER: T

____   A measurement made with a slightly damaged ruler would be
precise but not accurate.

7) TYPE: T   LEVEL: 1   TEXT REFERENCE: 3-8
ANSWER: F

____   The absolute uncertainty of a measurement is usually the same
as the relative uncertainty.

8) TYPE: T   LEVEL: 1   TEXT REFERENCE: 3-9
ANSWER: T

____   The number of significant digits of a number in exponential
form is represented in the decimal part.

9) TYPE: T   LEVEL: 1   TEXT REFERENCE: 3-10
ANSWER: F

_____   In adding measurements, the answer should be rounded to have
        the same number of digits as the smaller number.

10) TYPE: T   LEVEL: 1   TEXT REFERENCE: 3-11
ANSWER: F

_____   When rounding, a rule to follow is: round to the smaller number
        if it is even, to the larger if it is odd.

11) TYPE: T   LEVEL: 1   TEXT REFERENCE: 3-12
ANSWER: T

_____   There are numbers that have no uncertainty.

12) TYPE: T   LEVEL: 2   TEXT REFERENCE: 3-14
ANSWER: F

_____   Using a table is the best way to present data because it
        always reveals the proportional relationships between the
        data.

13) TYPE: T   LEVEL: 1   TEXT REFERENCE: 3-14
ANSWER: T

_____   Different relationships between data may be shown by
        rearranging data in a data table.

14) TYPE: T   LEVEL: 1   TEXT REFERENCE: 3-15
ANSWER: T

_____   Graphs are very useful to show proportional relationships
        between data.

15) TYPE: T   LEVEL: 1   TEXT REFERENCE: 3-15
ANSWER: T

_____   On a precise graph the best-fit line is located by using a
        mathematical equation.

16) TYPE: O   LEVEL: 1   TEXT REFERENCE: 3-1
ANSWER: inverse

Every unitary rate has a(n) _____ that also describes
a unitary rate.

17) TYPE: O   LEVEL: 1   TEXT REFERENCE: 3-2
ANSWER: exponential

A number such as 45^3 is called a(n) _____
number.

18) TYPE: O   LEVEL: 2   TEXT REFERENCE: 3-2
ANSWER: 4.53×10^{-4}

The number 0.000453 expressed in scientific notation equals
_____.

19) TYPE: O   LEVEL: 1   TEXT REFERENCE: 3-3
ANSWER: subtracting

The quotient of two powers of ten is obtained by _____
the exponents.

20) TYPE: O   LEVEL: 2   TEXT REFERENCE: 3-4
ANSWER: zero

The number (2×10^3) subtracted from (20×10^2) equals
_____.

21) TYPE: O   LEVEL: 3   TEXT REFERENCE: 3-5
ANSWER: decimal

The number system used by most people in everyday life is the
_____ system.

22) TYPE: O   LEVEL: 3   TEXT REFERENCE: 3-5
ANSWER: binary

The number 3 in the decimal system is the same as the number 11 in
the _____ system.

23) TYPE: O   LEVEL: 1   TEXT REFERENCE: 3-6
ANSWER: Avogadro's

The number of hydrogen atoms in one gram of hydrogen, or 6.02×10^{23} is called _____ number.

24) TYPE: O   LEVEL: 1   TEXT REFERENCE: 3-7
ANSWER: micrometer

A(n) _____ is an instrument which can measure a
thickness to the nearest thousandth of a centimeter.

25) TYPE: 0   LEVEL: 1   TEXT REFERENCE: 3-8
ANSWER: accuracy

How close a measurement is to the true value is called
_____.

26) TYPE: 0   LEVEL: 1   TEXT REFERENCE: 3-9
ANSWER: significant

In a measurement all certain digits plus the one uncertain digit are
called the _____ digits.

27) TYPE: 0   LEVEL: 1   TEXT REFERENCE: 3-9
ANSWER: magnitude

Scientific quantities always express both uncertainty and
_____.

28) TYPE: 0   LEVEL: 2   TEXT REFERENCE: 3-10
ANSWER: 7

The product of 2.3 and 3 should be expressed as _____.

29) TYPE: 0   LEVEL: 1   TEXT REFERENCE: 3-11
ANSWER: even

A good rule to follow when rounding numbers is "round to make the
uncertain digit_____".

30) TYPE: 0   LEVEL: 2   TEXT REFERENCE: 3-12
ANSWER: uncertainty

When numbers with no _____ are used in calculations
they do not affect the number of significant digits in the answer.

31) TYPE: 0   LEVEL: 1   TEXT REFERENCE: 3-15
ANSWER: tables

Graphs, pictures, and physical models many times reveal relationships
between data that _____ do not.

32) TYPE: 0   LEVEL: 1   TEXT REFERENCE: 3-16
ANSWER: slope

The _____ of a line tells how much the value plotted on
the y-axis increases as the x value is increased by one.

33) TYPE: O   LEVEL: 1   TEXT REFERENCE: 3-17
ANSWER: density

The ratio of mass to volume defines _____.

34) TYPE: O   LEVEL: 1   TEXT REFERENCE: 3-17
ANSWER: intensive

Properties that depend on the amount of material measured are called
_____ properties.

35) TYPE: O   LEVEL: 1   TEXT REFERENCE: 3-17
ANSWER: volume

In SI, the inverse of density is a unitary rate known as the specific
_____.

36) TYPE: M   LEVEL: 2   TEXT REFERENCE: 3-1
ANSWER: A

What is the unitary rate if there are six notches per two meters?

A. 3 notches per meter
B. 3 meters per notch
C. 12 notches per meter
D. 3 meters

37) TYPE: M   LEVEL: 2   TEXT REFERENCE: 3-2
ANSWER: D

The number twenty-three thousand expressed in proper scientific
notation is:

A. 23 000.
B. 23.000×10^3.
C. 2.3×10^3.
D. 2.3×10^4.

38) TYPE: M   LEVEL: 2   TEXT REFERENCE: 3-2
ANSWER: C

The expression "1.2 multiplied by ten to the third" is equal to:

A. $1.2 \times 10 \times 3$.   C. 1.2×10^3.
B. $(1.2 \times 10) \times 3$.   D. 1.2×3^{10}.

39) TYPE: M   LEVEL: 2   TEXT REFERENCE: 3-3
ANSWER: D

The quotient of 14×10^3 divided by 28×10^6 equals:

A. 2×10^3.
B. 2×10^{-3}.

C. 5.0×10^4.
D. 5.0×10^{-4}.

40) TYPE: M   LEVEL: 2   TEXT REFERENCE: 3-4
ANSWER: D

Adding (4.5×10^6) and (30.0×10^5) equals:

A. not possible.
B. 34.5×10^{30}.

C. 34.5×10^{11}.
D. 7.5×10^6.

41) TYPE: M   LEVEL: 1   TEXT REFERENCE: 3-6
ANSWER: A

Avogadro's number measures:

A. the number of hydrogen atoms in one gram of hydrogen.
B. the number of grams of hydrogen in one mole.
C. the number of grams of hydrogen in one atom of hydrogen.
D. the number of hydrogen moles in one gram of hydrogen.

42) TYPE: M   LEVEL: 2   TEXT REFERENCE: 3-8
ANSWER: D

A measurement with high precision has:

A. low uncertainty.
B. low accuracy.

C. high accuracy.
D. both A and C.

43) TYPE: M   LEVEL: 2   TEXT REFERENCE: 3-8
ANSWER: A

A distance measured as 43.50 mm with an uncertainty, of plus or minus
0.02 mm has a relative uncertainty of:

A. 0.000 459 7 mm.
B. 43.52 mm.

C. 43.48 mm.
D. 0.87 mm.

44) TYPE: M   LEVEL: 2   TEXT REFERENCE: 3-9
ANSWER: B

The number of significant digits in the number 23.567×10^5 is:

A. 3.
B. 5.

C. 4.
D. 10.

45) TYPE: M   LEVEL: 2   TEXT REFERENCE: 3-9
ANSWER: A

The uncertainty of the number 56.000 is represented by:

A. The last digit.
B. The last three digits.
C. The digit to the left of the decimal.
D. The digit to the right of the decimal.

46) TYPE: M   LEVEL: 2   TEXT REFERENCE: 3-9
ANSWER: B

The number 456 000 written with four significant digits is:

A. 456 000.   C. 4.560×10^{-5}.
B. 4.560×10^{5}.   D. 4.5600×10^{5}.

47) TYPE: M   LEVEL: 2   TEXT REFERENCE: 3-9
ANSWER: D

The uncertain digit in any number is:

A. The digit to the left of the decimal.
B. The digit to the right of the decimal.
C. The first digit.
D. The last digit.

48) TYPE: M   LEVEL: 2   TEXT REFERENCE: 3-10
ANSWER: D

The rounded product of 45.67 and 23.1 will contain how many
significant digits?

A. 4   C. 7
B. 3   D. 2

49) TYPE: M   LEVEL: 2   TEXT REFERENCE: 3-10
ANSWER: C

The number obtained by adding 6.7, 4.5, 1.0 and 6.4 should be
expressed as:

A. 18.0.   C. 18.6.
B. 18.5.   D. 19.0.

50) TYPE: M   LEVEL: 2   TEXT REFERENCE: 3-11
ANSWER: D

The product of 11.8 and 2.1 should be rounded to:

A. 24.8.   C. 24.5.
B. 24.7.   D. 25.

51) TYPE: M   LEVEL: 2   TEXT REFERENCE: 3-12
ANSWER: A

The number of inches in a foot has how many uncertain digits?

A. zero   C. six
B. one   D. twelve

52) TYPE: M   LEVEL: 2   TEXT REFERENCE: 3-12
ANSWER: A

The number of donut holes in a dozen donuts has an uncertainty of:

A. 0.   C. 6.
B. 1.   D. 12.

53) TYPE: M   LEVEL: 3   TEXT REFERENCE: 3-13
ANSWER: D

In 1977 the National Bureau of Standards redetermined the triple
point of mercury because:

A. mercury had become more dense.
B. mercury had become less dense.
C. the standard of measurement was improved.
D. the precision of measurement was improved.

54) TYPE: M   LEVEL: 2   TEXT REFERENCE: 3-15
ANSWER: D

Which of the following is not a characteristic of a good graph?

A. a descriptive title
B. points located by a small circle around them
C. labels on each axis which indicate units
D. lines drawn from point to point

55) TYPE: M   LEVEL: 2   TEXT REFERENCE: 3-16
ANSWER: A

If the coordinates of two points on a graph are (10 m, 4 s) and
(6 m, 2 s) what is the slope of the line?

A. 2   C. 0.5
B. 4   D. 16/6

56) TYPE: M   LEVEL: 2   TEXT REFERENCE: 3 16
ANSWER: B

Which of the following is not commonly used to calculate the slope of
a line?

A. data from a table
B. delta-x divided by delta-y
C. the slope of a parallel line
D. a graph of the line

57) TYPE: M   LEVEL: 2   TEXT REFERENCE: 3-16
ANSWER: A

The slope of a line is a(n):

A. unitary rate.   C. SI base unit.
B. unitary quantity.   D. none of these.

58) TYPE: M   LEVEL: 1   TEXT REFERENCE: 3-16
ANSWER: C

The slope of a line can be calculated using:

A. delta-x divided by delta-y.
B. delta-x multiplied by delta-y.
C. delta-y divided by delta-x.
D. delta-y multiplied by delta-x.

59) TYPE: M   LEVEL: 2   TEXT REFERENCE: 3-17
ANSWER: C

If the density of a substance is 6.45 g/cm^3 the specific volume is:

A. 6.45 g.   C. 0.155 cm^3/g.
B. 0.155 cm^3.   D. 6.45 g/cm^3.

60) TYPE: M   LEVEL: 1   TEXT REFERENCE: 3-17
ANSWER: B

Mass is a(n):

A. intensive property.
B. extensive property.
C. ratio of density to volume.
D. ratio of volume to density.

61) TYPE: M   LEVEL: 4   TEXT REFERENCE: LA
ANSWER: D

What is the best estimate and uncertainty for the numbers 42.57, 42.56, 42.58, and 42.60?

A. 45.57 ± 0.03.   C. 45.57 ± 0.01.
B. 42.58 ± 0.01.   D. 42.57 ± 0.03.

62) TYPE: M   LEVEL: 4   TEXT REFERENCE: LA
ANSWER: C

The volume of a sheet of plastic would be found by:

A. multiplying the length by the width.
B. multiplying the mass by the density.
C. dividing the mass by the density.
D. dividing the mass by the area.

63) TYPE: M   LEVEL: 4   TEXT REFERENCE: LB
ANSWER: C

What is the thickness of a material that spreads over an area of 300.0 cm^2 and has a volume of 0.050 cm^3?

A. 2.5×10^{-4} cm   C. 1.6×10^{-4} cm
B. 2.5×10^{-5} cm   D. 1.6×10^{-5} cm

64) TYPE: M   LEVEL: 4   TEXT REFERENCE: LB.
ANSWER: A

If there are 32 drops of a liquid in 1 cm^3, what is the volume of one drop of liquid?

A. 3.1×10^{-2} cm^3 C. 3.1×10^{-1} cm^3
B. 3.1×10^{-3} cm^3 D. 3.1 cm^3

65) TYPE: M   LEVEL: 4   TEXT REFERENCE: LB
ANSWER: C

If the volume of one drop of a pure liquid is 2.4×10^{-2} cm^3, what is the volume of pure liquid in one drop of a 0.5% solution?

A. 1.2×10^{-1} cm^3 C. 1.2×10^{-4} cm^3
B. 1.2×10^{4} cm^3 D. 1.2×10^{-2} cm^3

66) TYPE: M   LEVEL: 4   TEXT REFERENCE: LC
ANSWER: A

If a graduated cylinder that has been rinsed with water but not dried is used to experimentally determine the density of mercury, the value obtained will be:

A. less than if you had used a clean container.
B. greater than if you had used a clean container.
C. the same as if you had used a clean container.
D. the density of water.

67) TYPE: M   LEVEL: 4   TEXT REFERENCE: LC
ANSWER: D

In an experiment using a 10 mL graduated cylinder, the value calculated for the densiity of the liquid being measured would be:

A. greater than a value calculated using a larger cylinder.
B. less than a value calculated using a larger cylinder.
C. greater than a value calculated using a smaller cylinder.
D. none of the above.

Chapter 4   THE MOLE

1) TYPE: T   LEVEL: 1   TEXT REFERENCE: 4-1
ANSWER: F

_____   A balance can be used to find the relative mass of an atom.

2) TYPE: T   LEVEL: 2   TEXT REFERENCE: 4-3
ANSWER: T

_____   The number of carbon-12 atoms in exactly 12.0000 g of carbon is Avogodro's number.

3) TYPE: T   LEVEL: 1   TEXT REFERENCE: 4-3
ANSWER: F

_____   One mole of a substance always has the same mass as one mole of another substance.

4) TYPE: T   LEVEL: 2   TEXT REFERENCE: 4-5
ANSWER: F

_____   The formula H_2O_2 represents a diatomic molecule.

5) TYPE: T   LEVEL: 1   TEXT REFERENCE: 4-6
ANSWER: T

_____   If you know the mass of a sample of an element, you can divide by the atomic mass to find the number of moles of that element in the sample.

6) TYPE: T   LEVEL: 2   TEXT REFERENCE: 4-7
ANSWER: T

_____   The formula Fe_2O_3 is an example of an empirical formula.

7) TYPE: T   LEVEL: 2   TEXT REFERENCE: 4-8
ANSWER: F

_____   The number 4.49, rounded to two digits, is 4.50.

8) TYPE: T   LEVEL: 1   TEXT REFERENCE: 4-9
ANSWER: F

_____   For most carbon compounds the molecular formula is the same as the empirical formula.

9) TYPE: T   LEVEL: 2   TEXT REFERENCE: 4-10
ANSWER: T

_____   The percent composition of oxygen is the same in a 4-g sample
        of a compound with 2 g of oxygen as in a 150-g sample of a
        compound with 75 g of oxygen.

10) TYPE: T   LEVEL: 1   TEXT REFERENCE: 4-11
ANSWER: F

_____   Concentration describes the amount of solute per volume of
        solvent.

11) TYPE: T   LEVEL: 1   TEXT REFERENCE: 4-11
ANSWER: F

_____   The molarity of a solution is always equal to the number of
        moles of solute in that solution.

12) TYPE: T   LEVEL: 1   TEXT REFERENCE: 4-12
ANSWER: T

_____   If moles of solute are plotted versus liters of solution on a
        graph, the slope of the resulting line indicates the molarity of
        the solution.

13) TYPE: T   LEVEL: 2   TEXT REFERENCE: 4-12
ANSWER: T

_____   The amount of sugar in 1 liter of a 1.0M solution is the same
        as the amount of sugar in 2 liters of a 0.5M solution.

14) TYPE: O   LEVEL: 1   TEXT REFERENCE: 4-1
ANSWER: relative

The _____ mass of an object is expressed by
comparing it mathematically to the mass of another object.

15) TYPE: O   LEVEL: 1   TEXT REFERENCE: 4-2
ANSWER: particles

Avogadro's hypothesis states that equal volumes of gases contain equal
numbers of _____.

16) TYPE: O   LEVEL: 1   TEXT REFERENCE: 4-3
ANSWER: mole

The amount of a substance that contains 6.02×10^{23} particles is
called a(n) _____.

17) TYPE: 0   LEVEL: 1   TEXT REFERENCE: 4-3
ANSWER: Avogadro's

The standard number of particles for one mole is called
_____ number.

18) TYPE: 0   LEVEL: 1   TEXT REFERENCE: 4-1
ANSWER: molar

The _____ mass of a compound is the sum of the atomic
masses of all elements in the compound.

19) TYPE: 0   LEVEL: 1   TEXT REFERENCE: 4-4
ANSWER: formula

The simplest formula that provides the smallest whole number ratio of
ions in a compound is sometimes referred to as the _____
unit.

20) TYPE: 0   LEVEL: 1   TEXT REFERENCE: 4-5
ANSWER: diatomic

A molecule with two atoms is called a(n) _____
molecule.

21) TYPE: 0   LEVEL: 1   TEXT REFERENCE: 4-6
ANSWER: moles

The mass of an element in a sample divided by the atomic mass of that
element will tell the number of _____ of that
element in the sample.

22) TYPE: 0   LEVEL: 1   TEXT REFERENCE: 4-7
ANSWER: empirical

A(n) _____ formula is one that is obtained from
experimental data and represents the smallest whole number ratio of
atoms in a compound.

23) TYPE: 0   LEVEL: 2   TEXT REFERENCE: 4-8
ANSWER: 5.0

The number 4.97 rounded to two digits is _____.

24) TYPE: O   LEVEL: 1   TEXT REFERENCE: 4-9
ANSWER: molecular

The _____ formula is always some multiple of the empirical formula.

25) **TYPE:** O   **LEVEL:** 2   **TEXT REFERENCE:** 4-10
ANSWER: 25

If three eggs out of a dozen are broken, _____ percent are broken.

26) **TYPE:** O   **LEVEL:** 2   **TEXT REFERENCE:** 4-10
ANSWER: 25

If a 64-g sample contains 16 g nickel and 48 g oxygen, it contains _____ percent nickel.

27) **TYPE:** O   **LEVEL:** 1   **TEXT REFERENCE:** 4-11
ANSWER: concentration

The amount of a solute in a given amount of substance is described by _____.

28) **TYPE:** O   **LEVEL:** 1   **TEXT REFERENCE:** 4-11
ANSWER: molarity

The concentration of a solution in moles per liter is described by _____.

29) **TYPE:** O   **LEVEL:** 2   **TEXT REFERENCE:** 4-12
ANSWER: 2

A 500-mL sample of a 2.0M solution contains _____ moles per liter.

30) **TYPE:** M   **LEVEL:** 2   **TEXT REFERENCE:** 4-1
ANSWER: C

What is the relative mass of donuts to cookies if one dozen donuts has a mass of 1500 g and the same number of cookies has a mass of 500 g?

A. 750 000   C. 3
B. 1000   D. 0.33

31) **TYPE:** M   **LEVEL:** 2   **TEXT REFERENCE:** 4-3
ANSWER: C

If the relative mass of marbles to ping-pong balls is 20 g, and ten marbles has a mass of 40 g, what is the mass of ten ping-pong balls?

A. 0.5 g
B. 800 g

C. 2 g
D. 0.2 g

32) **TYPE:** M   **LEVEL:** 2   **TEXT REFERENCE:** 4-3
ANSWER: A

How many moles of pebbles do you have if you have 12.04×10^{23} pebbles?

A. 2 mol
B. 2×10^{23} mol

C. 6.02×10^{23} mol
D. 0.5 mol

33) **TYPE:** M   **LEVEL:** 2   **TEXT REFERENCE:** 4-3
ANSWER: B

If a sealed flask contains 3.01×10^{24} nitrogen dioxide molecules, how many moles of oxygen atoms are in the flask?

A. 1×10^{23} mol
B. 1×10^{3} mol

C. 0.5×10^{3} mol
D. 2×10^{3} mol

34) **TYPE:** M   **LEVEL:** 2   **TEXT REFERENCE:** 4-3
ANSWER: D

How many peanuts are in a 500-g bag if the atomic mass of a peanut is 10 amu?

A. 8.3×10^{23} peanuts
B. 2.0×10^{21} peanuts

C. 5.0×10^{24} peanuts
D. 3.01×10^{25} peanuts

35) **TYPE:** M   **LEVEL:** 1   **TEXT REFERENCE:** 4-3
ANSWER: D

Which of the following is not true about one mole?

A. 1 mole contains Avogadro's number of particles.
B. "mole" is abbreviated mol.

C. 12 g of carbon equals one mole of carbon atoms.
D. The mass of 1 mol of calcium = mass of 1 mol of sodium.

Chapter 4   THE MOLE

36) TYPE: M   LEVEL: 1   TEXT REFERENCE: 4-4
ANSWER: C

When the atomic masses of the elements in a compound are added, the resulting quantity is called a(n):

A. formula unit.   C. molar mass.
B. atomic mass unit.   D. relative mass.

37) TYPE: M   LEVEL: 1   TEXT REFERENCE: 4-4
ANSWER: A

The smallest whole number ratio of ions in a compound is sometimes called the:

A. formula unit.   C. molar mass.
B. atomic mass unit.   D. relative mass.

38) TYPE: M   LEVEL: 1   TEXT REFERENCE: 4-5
ANSWER: C

What is the diatomic form of chlorine?

A. 2Cl   C. Cl_2
B. Cl   D. $2Cl_2$

39) TYPE: M   LEVEL: 1   TEXT REFERENCE: 4-5
ANSWER: A

Which of the following is incorrect?

A. mass of 1 mol oxygen atoms > mass of 1 mol O_2
B. mass of 1 mol oxygen atoms < mass of 1 mol O_2
C. mass of 1 mol oxygen gas > mass of 1 mol of oxygen alone
D. mass of 1 molecule of O_2 < mass of 1 mol O_2

40) TYPE: M   LEVEL: 2   TEXT REFERENCE: 4-5
ANSWER: C

If the mass of one mole of oxygen atoms is 16.0 g, what is the mass of one mole of oxygen gas?

A. 16.0 g   C. 32.0 g
B. 8.0 g   D. 2.0 g

41) TYPE: M   LEVEL: 2   TEXT REFERENCE: 4-6
ANSWER: B

Which of the following is a unit factor for oxygen, whose atomic mass
is sixteen g/mol?

A. 16 g of O/6.02 mol of O
B. 16 g of O/1 mol of O
C. 1 g of O/6.02 mol of O
D. 1 g of O_2

42) TYPE: M   LEVEL: 2   TEXT REFERENCE: 4-6
ANSWER: C

How many atoms are in a sample of zinc that contains 0.001 moles Zn?

A. 1 000   C. 6.02×10^{20}
B. 6.02×10^{23} D. 6.02×10^{26}

43) TYPE: M   LEVEL: 2   TEXT REFERENCE: 4-7
ANSWER: D

Which of the following represents an empirical formula?

A. C_2O_4
B. 50 g carbon - 10 g carbon = 40 g carbon
C. dinitrogen tetrachloride
D. NO_2

44) TYPE: M   LEVEL: 1   TEXT REFERENCE: 4-8
ANSWER: D

The number 1.28 rounded to two digits is:

A. 1.2.   C. 1.5.
B. 1.30.   D. 1.3.

45) TYPE: M   LEVEL: 1   TEXT REFERENCE: 4-9
ANSWER: C

The molecular formula is always a multiple of the:

A. molar mass.   C. empirical formula.
B. atomic weight.   D. diatomic formula.

Chapter 4   THE MOLE

What is the molecular formula of a compound composed of 2 g of hydrogen and 32 g of oxygen, with a molecular mass of 34 g?

A. HO   C. H_2O
B. H_2O_2 D. H_4O_4

What is the percentage of sodium in a 42-g sample of a compound that contains 7 g of Na and 35 g of Cl?

A. 0.16%   C. 84%
B. 16%   D. 0.84%

What is the percent by mass of hydrogen in water?

A. 11%   C. 88%
B. 0.115   D. 5%

Molarity describes the concentration of a solution in terms of:

A. liters per mole.   C. moles per liter.
B. mass per liters.   D. mass per moles.

How many moles of HCl are in 1.75 L of a 4.25M solution?

A. 7.45   C. 2.42
B. 14.87   D. 0.41

51) TYPE: M   LEVEL: 1   TEXT REFERENCE: 4-12
ANSWER: D

The volume of water used to prepare a 1.0M sugar solution is less
than the volume of water used to prepare a 1.0M methanol solution
because of which factor?

A. size of the solute's molecules
B. molecular attraction
C. shape of the molecules
D. all of the above

52) TYPE: M   LEVEL: 1   TEXT REFERENCE: 4-12
ANSWER: C

The molarity of a solution remains constant, regardless of:

A. concentration of solute.
B. concentration of solvent.
C. shape of the molecules.
D. all of the above.

53) TYPE: O   LEVEL: 4   TEXT REFERENCE: LB
ANSWER: decant

To pour off only the liquid from a container that is holding both a
solid and a liquid is to _____.

54) TYPE: O   LEVEL: 4   TEXT REFERENCE: LC
ANSWER: $MgCl_2$

The empirical formula for magnesium chloride is _____.

55) TYPE: O   LEVEL: 4   TEXT REFERENCE: LD
ANSWER: $CuSO_4$

The formula for the anhydrous form of the compound $CuSO_4$ is
_____.

56) TYPE: M   LEVEL: 4   TEXT REFERENCE: LA
ANSWER: C

Acid is neutralized by the addition of:

A. blue litmus paper.   C. a hydroxide.
B. Mg.   D. HCl.

57) TYPE: M   LEVEL: 4   TEXT REFERENCE: LA
ANSWER: A

How many characteristic properties of two substances must be different for the two substances to be different?

A. one   C. more than two
B. two   D. zero

58) TYPE: M   LEVEL: 4   TEXT REFERENCE: LB
ANSWER: A

How many moles of copper would be produced by reacting 25.0 g of iron with an unlimited supply of copper (II) chloride solution?

A. 0.448 mol   C. 1.642 mol
B. 2.230 mol   D. 1395 mol

59) TYPE: M   LEVEL: 4   TEXT REFERENCE: LC
ANSWER: B

If in a reaction between Mg and HCl the theoretical yield is 5.43 g $MgCl_2$, and the actual yield is 5.45 g $MgCl_2$, which of the following could be an explanation for the difference?

A. Some magnesium was   C. Too much HCl was added.
   poured out of the
   beaker.
B. There was an error   D. All of the above.
   in the initial mea-
   surement of Mg.

60) TYPE: M   LEVEL: 4   TEXT REFERENCE: A
ANSWER: B

Which of the following substances is anhydrous?

A. copper sulfate   C. copper sulfate
   heptahydrate   pentahydrate
B. copper sulfate   D. both B and C

1) TYPE: T   LEVEL: 1   TEXT REFERENCE: 5-2
ANSWER: F

_____ The number of atoms of each substance before a chemical
      reaction is always greater than the number of atoms after the
      reaction.

2) TYPE: T   LEVEL: 2   TEXT REFERENCE: 5-2
ANSWER: T

_____ In the decomposition of water, twice as many hydrogen atoms as
      oxygen atoms are produced.

3) TYPE: T   LEVEL: 1   TEXT REFERENCE: 5-3
ANSWER: F

_____ The law of conservation of mass holds true even if atoms are
      lost or gained in a reaction.

4) TYPE: T   LEVEL: 1   TEXT REFERENCE: 5-4
ANSWER: F

_____ In a chemical equation, the products are found on the left side
      of the equation, and the reactants on the right side.

5) TYPE: T   LEVEL: 1   TEXT REFERENCE: 5-5
ANSWER: F

_____ In order to balance a chemical equation, it is helpful to
      change the subscripts of the products and the reactants.

6) TYPE: T   LEVEL: 1   TEXT REFERENCE: 5-6
ANSWER: T

_____ The symbol (aq) means "dissolved in water."

7) TYPE: T   LEVEL: 2   TEXT REFERENCE: 5-6
ANSWER: T

_____ The symbol $2CO_2$ is read "two molecules of carbon dioxide."

8) TYPE: T   LEVEL: 2   TEXT REFERENCE: 5-7
ANSWER: F

_____ The formation of hydrocarbons is an example of combustion.

9) TYPE: T   LEVEL: 1   TEXT REFERENCE: 5-7
ANSWER: F

_____ Compounds made of water and carbon are called hydrocarbons.

10) TYPE: T   LEVEL: 1   TEXT REFERENCE: 5-7
ANSWER: T

_____ Hydrogen is not as active an element as calcium.

11) TYPE: T   LEVEL: 1   TEXT REFERENCE: 5-7
ANSWER: F

_____ Water is a reactant in a water-forming chemical reaction.

12) TYPE: T   LEVEL: 1   TEXT REFERENCE: 5-8
ANSWER: T

_____ In a chemical equation, the arrow always points in the
direction of change.

13) TYPE: T   LEVEL: 1   TEXT REFERENCE: 5-9
ANSWER: T

_____ Combustion is an example of an exothermic chemical reaction.

14) TYPE: T   LEVEL: 1   TEXT REFERENCE: 5-10
ANSWER: F

_____ Energy is a product in endothermic reactions.

15) TYPE: T   LEVEL: 2   TEXT REFERENCE: 5-11
ANSWER: F

_____ Iron rusts slower in water than in air.

16) TYPE: O   LEVEL: 1   TEXT REFERENCE: 5-1
ANSWER: identity

A chemical equation describes the _____ of pure
substances before and after chemical change.

17) TYPE: O   LEVEL: 1   TEXT REFERENCE: 5-2
ANSWER: one

Water is produced when two volumes of hydrogen gas combine with
_____ volume(s) of oxygen gas.

18) TYPE: O   LEVEL: 1   TEXT REFERENCE: 5-2
ANSWER: formation

The chemical change that occurs during the decomposition of water is
exactly opposite the chemical change that occurs during the
_____ of water.

19) TYPE: O   LEVEL: 1   TEXT REFERENCE: 5-3
ANSWER: conservation

The law of _____ of mass states that the total
mass of products equals the total mass of reactants.

20) TYPE: O   LEVEL: 1   TEXT REFERENCE: 5-4
ANSWER: reactants

In a chemical equation, the chemicals to the left of the arrow are
called _____.

21) TYPE: O   LEVEL: 2   TEXT REFERENCE: 5-5
ANSWER: 2KOH

The balanced equation for the reaction of potassium and water to
produce potassium hydroxide and hydrogen is $2K + 2H_2O \rightarrow$
_____ $+ H_2$

22) TYPE: O   LEVEL: 1   TEXT REFERENCE: 5-5
ANSWER: coefficients

Numbers in front of the formulas in an equation are called
_____.

23) TYPE: O   LEVEL: 1   TEXT REFERENCE: 5-6
ANSWER: $\rightarrow$

The symbol _____ is read "yields" or "produces".

24) TYPE: O   LEVEL: 1   TEXT REFERENCE: 5-6
ANSWER: aqueous/dissolved in water

The symbol (aq) is read _____.

25) TYPE: O   LEVEL: 1   TEXT REFERENCE: 5-7
ANSWER: synthesis

The combination of two or more substances to form a compound is a(n)
_____ reaction.

Chapter 5   CHEMICAL REACTIONS

26) TYPE: 0   LEVEL: 1   TEXT REFERENCE: 5-7
ANSWER: combustion

A chemical reaction that gives off a large amount of energy in the
form of heat and light is _____.

27) TYPE: 0   LEVEL: 1   TEXT REFERENCE: 5-7
ANSWER: activity

The _____ of an element is a measure of its ability
to replace another element in a compound.

28) TYPE: 0   LEVEL: 1   TEXT REFERENCE: 5-7
ANSWER: decomposition

The general equation AB → A + B describes a _____
reaction.

29) TYPE: 0   LEVEL: 2   TEXT REFERENCE: 5-8
ANSWER: $4H_2O$

The balanced equation for the combustion of C_6H_6 is:
       $C_6H_6 + 8O_2 → 6CO_2 +$ _____.

30) TYPE: 0   LEVEL: 1   TEXT REFERENCE: 5-9
ANSWER: exothermic

A chemical reaction that releases energy to the surroundings is called
_____.

31) TYPE: 0   LEVEL: 1   TEXT REFERENCE: 5-10
ANSWER: endothermic

A chemical reaction that absorbs energy from the environment is
called _____.

32) TYPE: 0   LEVEL: 1   TEXT REFERENCE: 5-11
ANSWER: nitrogen

Air is made up of about 20 percent oxygen and 80 percent
_____.

33) TYPE: M   LEVEL: 1   TEXT REFERENCE: 5-2
ANSWER: C

A method used to decompose water is:

A. addition of hydrogen.   C. electrolysis.
B. addition of nitric acid.   D. addition of hydrogen gas.

34) TYPE: M   LEVEL: 1   TEXT REFERENCE: 5-2
ANSWER: B

Decomposition of water results in one part oxygen gas to:

A. one part hydrogen gas.
B. two parts hydrogen gas.
C. two parts liquid hydrogen.
D. one part liquid hydrogen.

35) TYPE: M   LEVEL: 2   TEXT REFERENCE: 5-4
ANSWER: A

In the decomposition of water, water is a(n):

A. reactant.   C. coefficient.
B. product.   D. electrode.

36) TYPE: M   LEVEL: 1   TEXT REFERENCE: 5-3
ANSWER: A

The law of conservation of mass states that the total mass of
reactants:

A. is equal to the total mass of products.
B. is less than the total mass of products.
C. is greater than the total mass of products.
D. is twice the total mass of products.

37) TYPE: M   LEVEL: 1   TEXT REFERENCE: 5-4
ANSWER: B

A substance formed from the combination of sodium and chlorine is
not:

A. a salt.   C. sodium chloride.
B. a reactant.   D. soluble in water.

38) TYPE: M   LEVEL: 1   TEXT REFERENCE: 5-5
ANSWER: D

The balanced equation that shows the reaction of carbon and oxygen to
form carbon monoxide is:

A. $C + O \rightarrow CO$.   C. $2C + 2O \rightarrow CO_2$.
B. $C + O \rightarrow CO_2$.   D. $2C + O_2 \rightarrow 2CO$.

39) TYPE: M   LEVEL: 2   TEXT REFERENCE: 5-5
ANSWER: C

The coefficient for potassium in the following equation should be:
$$K + 2H_2O \rightarrow 2KOH + H_2$$

A. 1.   C. 2.
B. 6.   D. 12.

40) TYPE: M   LEVEL: 2   TEXT REFERENCE: 5-5
ANSWER: B

The balanced equation for the reaction of hydrochloric acid and
oxygen to produce chlorine and water is:

A. $2HCl + O_2 \rightarrow Cl_2 + H_2O$.
B. $4HCl + O_2 \rightarrow 2Cl_2 + 2H_2O$.
C. $2HCl + O_2 \rightarrow 2Cl_2 + H_2O$.
D. $2HCl + 2O \rightarrow 2Cl + H_2O$.

41) TYPE: M   LEVEL: 2   TEXT REFERENCE: 5-6
ANSWER: C

The word equation "iron reacts with oxygen to produce iron (II)
oxide" is the same as which of these balanced equations?

A. $I + O_2 \rightarrow IO_2$
B. $Fe + O_2 \rightarrow FeO_2$
C. $2Fe + O_2 \rightarrow 2FeO$
D. $2Fe + O_2 \rightarrow FeO_2$

42) TYPE: M   LEVEL: 1   TEXT REFERENCE: 5-6
ANSWER: B

The symbol N.R. means:

A. no reactants.   C. not reacting.
B. no reaction.   D. not ready.

43) TYPE: M   LEVEL: 2   TEXT REFERENCE: 5-7
ANSWER: C

A replacement reaction involving an element that is being replaced by
a less active element would:

A. proceed rapidly.
B. proceed very slowly.
C. not occur.
D. occur under certain conditions.

44) TYPE: M   LEVEL: 1   TEXT REFERENCE: 5-7
ANSWER: D

The general formula A + BC → AC + B represents:

A. synthesis.   C. double replacement.
B. decomposition.   D. single replacement.

45) TYPE: M   LEVEL: 2   TEXT REFERENCE: 5-7
ANSWER: C

Which of the following is a double replacement reaction?

A. $Fe + CuSO_4 \rightarrow FeSO_4 + Cu$
B. $2K + 2H_2O \rightarrow 2KOH + H_2O$
C. $Mg_3N_2 + 3H_2O \rightarrow 3MgO + 2NH_3$
D. $2NH_4Cl + Ca(OH)_2 \rightarrow 2NH_3 + 2H_2O + CaCl_2$

46) TYPE: M   LEVEL: 2   TEXT REFERENCE: 5-7
ANSWER: C

Which of the following is not true about a combustion reaction?

A. heat is given off   C. water is added
B. oxygen is added   D. light is given off

47) TYPE: M   LEVEL: 1   TEXT REFERENCE: 5-7
ANSWER: D

The general form for a single replacement reaction is:

A. A + B → AB.
B. AB + XY → AY + BX.
C. AB → A + B.
D. A + BC → AC + B.

48) TYPE: M   LEVEL: 2   TEXT REFERENCE: 5-8
ANSWER: B

What is the equation for the synthesis reaction to produce magnesium
chloride?

A. $Mg + Cl \rightarrow MgCl$
B. $Mg + Cl_2 \rightarrow MgCl_2$
C. $2Mg + Cl_2 \rightarrow 2MgCl$
D. $MgCl_2 \rightarrow Mg + Cl_2$

Chapter 5   CHEMICAL REACTIONS

49) TYPE: M   LEVEL: 2   TEXT REFERENCE: 5-8
ANSWER: D

The equation for the combustion of C_4H_{12} is:

A. $2C_2 + 12H \rightarrow C_4H12$.
B. $C_4H_{12} + 7O_2 \rightarrow 2C_2 + 6H_2O$.
C. $C_4H_{12} + O_2 \rightarrow CO_2 + 6H_2O$.
D. $C_4H_{12} + 7O_2 \rightarrow 4CO_2 + 6H_2O$.

50) TYPE: M   LEVEL: 2   TEXT REFERENCE: 5-8
ANSWER: D

What is the equation for the replacement of aluminum by magnesium in aluminum fluoride?

A. $Mg + AlF_3 \rightarrow MgF_2 + Al$
B. $Al + MgF_3 \rightarrow AlF_2 + Mg$
C. $3Al + 2MgF_3 \rightarrow 3AlF_2 + 2Mg$
D. $3Mg + 2AlF_3 \rightarrow 3MgF_2 + 2Al$

51) TYPE: M   LEVEL: 2   TEXT REFERENCE: 5-9
ANSWER: C

Which of the following is an exothermic, single-replacement reaction?

A. $Cl_2 + 2NaI \rightarrow 2NaCl + I_2$
B. energy $+ Cl_2 + 2NaI \rightarrow 2NaCl + I_2$
C. $Cl_2 + 2NaI \rightarrow 2NaCl + I_2 +$ energy
D. $2Ca + O_2 \rightarrow 2CaO +$ energy

52) TYPE: M   LEVEL: 2   TEXT REFERENCE: 5-10
ANSWER: D

The equation $MgCO_3(s) +$ energy $\rightarrow MgO(s) + CO_2(g)$ is a(n):

A. combustion reaction.
B. exothermic decomposition reaction.
C. endothermic synthesis reaction.
D. endothermic decomposition reaction.

53) TYPE: M   LEVEL: 2   TEXT REFERENCE: 5-11
ANSWER: B

The combination of iron with oxygen gas to produce iron oxide is a:

A. combustion reaction.
B. reaction that produces rust.
C. reaction that powers an automobile.
D. by-product of electrolysis.

54) TYPE: O   LEVEL: 4   TEXT REFERENCE: LA
ANSWER: $2Na_3PO_4$

Complete the following balanced reaction:
   $3Na_2CO_3 + 2H_3PO_4 \rightarrow 3H_2O + 3CO_2 +$ _____.

55) TYPE: O   LEVEL: 4   TEXT REFERENCE: LB
ANSWER: HCl

Complete the following balanced reaction:
                  $Cu +$ _____ $\rightarrow$ N.R.

56) TYPE: M   LEVEL: 4   TEXT REFERENCE: LA
ANSWER: A

What is the formula for sodium carbonate?

A. Na_2CO_3 C. S_2CO_3
B. $NaCO$ D. Na_3CO_3

57) TYPE: M   LEVEL: 4   TEXT REFERENCE: LA
ANSWER: B

What is the balanced equation for the reaction between calcium
carbonate and hydrochloric acid?

A. $CaCO_3 + HCl \rightarrow CaCl_2 + CO_2$
B. $CaCO_3 + 2HCl \rightarrow CaCl_2 + CO_2 + H_2O$
C. $CaCO_3 + 2HCl \rightarrow CaCl_2 + CO_2$
D. $CaCO_3 + HCl \rightarrow CaCl_2 + CO_2 + H_2O$

58) TYPE: M   LEVEL: 4   TEXT REFERENCE: LB
ANSWER: D

What may affect the rate at which a metal reacts with an acid, other
than the activity of the metal?

A. concentration of the acid
B. stirring
C. surface area of the metal
D. all of the above

59) TYPE: M   LEVEL: 4   TEXT REFERENCE: LB
ANSWER: A

The correct order for the following metals, in order of decreasing
reactivity, is:

A. Mg, Zn, Fe, Cu   C. Mg, Zn, Cu, Fe
B. Cu, Fe, Zn, Mg   D. Cu, Fe, Mg, Zn

1) TYPE: T   LEVEL: 1   TEXT REFERENCE: 6-1
ANSWER: T

_____   One way in which cooking and chemistry are similar is that
both recipes and chemical equations describe proportional
relationships between the ingredients or reactants.

2) TYPE: T   LEVEL: 1   TEXT REFERENCE: 6-2
ANSWER: F

_____   The mole ratio may be obtained using the coefficients from
either a balanced or unbalanced equation.

3) TYPE: T   LEVEL: 1   TEXT REFERENCE: 6-2
ANSWER: F

_____   The mole ratio becomes larger or smaller depending on the
amounts of each substance used in the reaction.

4) TYPE: T   LEVEL: 2   TEXT REFERENCE: 6-3
ANSWER: F

_____   In the equation, 2 mol Be + 1 mol O_2 → 2 mol BeO, the
ratio of grams Be to grams O is 2 to 1.

5) TYPE: T   LEVEL: 1   TEXT REFERENCE: 6-4
ANSWER: T

_____   The word "stoichiometry" literally means "to measure elements."

6) TYPE: T   LEVEL: 2   TEXT REFERENCE: 6-5
ANSWER: T

_____   9.4 moles of sodium metal would react with chlorine gas to
make 550 grams of sodium chloride.

7) TYPE: T   LEVEL: 1   TEXT REFERENCE: 6-6
ANSWER: F

_____   In a balanced equation, the mass ratio is the same as the mole
ratio.

8) TYPE: T   LEVEL: 1   TEXT REFERENCE: 6-7
ANSWER: T

_____   Molarity expresses the number of moles of a dissolved substance
per liter of solution.

Chapter 6 CALCULATIONS INVOLVING REACTIONS

9) TYPE: T   LEVEL: 1   TEXT REFERENCE: 6-8
ANSWER: F

_____ The limiting reactant is usually the reactant added in excess to insure all the other reactants are used up.

10) TYPE: T   LEVEL: 1   TEXT REFERENCE: 6-8
ANSWER: F

_____ The limiting reactant is usually the least expensive, most easily recovered chemical in a reaction.

11) TYPE: T   LEVEL: 3   TEXT REFERENCE: 6-9
ANSWER: T

_____ The percent yield is obtained by dividing the actual yield by the theoretical yield.

12) TYPE: T   LEVEL: 3   TEXT REFERENCE: 6-9
ANSWER: F

_____ The actual yield is usually greater than the theoretical yield.

13) TYPE: T   LEVEL: 3   TEXT REFERENCE: 6-9
ANSWER: T

_____ The percent yield is often less than 100%.

14) TYPE: O   LEVEL: 1   TEXT REFERENCE: 6-2
ANSWER: mole

In a chemical equation, the combining ratio is the same as the _____ ratio of the combining substances.

15) TYPE: O   LEVEL: 1   TEXT REFERENCE: 6-2
ANSWER: amount/mass

The mole ratio can be used to predict the _____ of one substance needed to react with another.

16) TYPE: O   LEVEL: 1   TEXT REFERENCE: 6-2
ANSWER: increase

If the amount of reactants in a chemical reaction is increased, the total amount of products will _____.

17) **TYPE:** 0   **LEVEL:** 1   **TEXT REFERENCE:** 6-3
ANSWER: mole

The coefficients in a balanced equation may be used to express the
_____ ratio of the reactants and products.

18) **TYPE:** 0   **LEVEL:** 1   **TEXT REFERENCE:** 6-4
ANSWER: stoichiometry

Measuring or calculating the amounts of substances in a reaction
involves the use of _____.

19) **TYPE:** 0   **LEVEL:** 1   **TEXT REFERENCE:** 6-4
ANSWER: mass

In the lab, substances are not measured in moles but in units that
describe _____.

20) **TYPE:** 0   **LEVEL:** 2   **TEXT REFERENCE:** 6-5
ANSWER: 17.6

To produce 737 grams of sodium fluoride, fluorine gas must react with
_____ moles of sodium metal.

21) **TYPE:** 0   **LEVEL:** 2   **TEXT REFERENCE:** 6-6
ANSWER: 58.4

The decomposition of 96 grams of potassium chlorate, $KClO_3$, produces
_____ grams of potassium chloride, KCl.

22) **TYPE:** 0   **LEVEL:** 1   **TEXT REFERENCE:** 6-6
ANSWER: grams

When determining the mass of each substance in a reaction, mole
ratios are used to convert the number of moles to _____.

23) **TYPE:** 0   **LEVEL:** 1   **TEXT REFERENCE:** 6-7
ANSWER: liter

Molarity expresses the number of moles of a dissolved substance per
_____ of solution.

24) **TYPE:** 0   **LEVEL:** 2   **TEXT REFERENCE:** 6-7
ANSWER: 0.425

The volume of a 425 mL KOH solution is equivalent to _____L.

25) TYPE: O   LEVEL: 1   TEXT REFERENCE: 6-8
ANSWER: excess

In order to completely use up one reactant, it is a common practice
to add another reactant in _____ of the necessary
amount.

26) TYPE: O   LEVEL: 1   TEXT REFERENCE: 6-8
ANSWER: limiting

The reactant that determines the amount of product obtained is called
the _____ reactant.

27) TYPE: O   LEVEL: 3   TEXT REFERENCE: 6-9
ANSWER: theoretical

The amount of a product obtainable under perfect conditions is called
the _____ yield.

28) TYPE: O   LEVEL: 3   TEXT REFERENCE: 6-9
ANSWER: percent

The number obtained by dividing the actual yield by the theoretical
yield is called the _____ yield.

29) TYPE: M   LEVEL: 2   TEXT REFERENCE: 6-2
ANSWER: B

How many moles of oxygen would be required to react with calcium to
produce six moles of calcium oxide?

A. 1   C. 6
B. 3   D. 2

30) TYPE: M   LEVEL: 2   TEXT REFERENCE: 6-2
ANSWER: B

In the following equation the unitary mole ratio of the reactants
potassium and chlorine is:

$$8K + 4Cl_2 \rightarrow 8KCl$$

A. 8 mol K/4 mol Cl_2.
B. 2 mol K/1 mol Cl_2.
C. 8 mol K/8 mol KCl
D. 4 mol Cl_2/8 mol KCl

31) TYPE: M   LEVEL: 2   TEXT REFERENCE: 6-2
ANSWER: B

If in the formation of sodium chloride the amounts of sodium and
chlorine reactants are doubled, the amount of NaCl produced will:

A. remain the same.   C. triple.
B. double.   D. be half as much.

32) TYPE: M   LEVEL: 2   TEXT REFERENCE: 6-3
ANSWER: C

In the equation 2 mol Ca + 1 mol O_2 → 2 mol CaO the gram ratio of
calcium to oxygen is:

A. 2/1.   C. 2.5/1.
B. 1/2.   D. 1/2.5.

33) TYPE: M   LEVEL: 2   TEXT REFERENCE: 6-3
ANSWER: A

The mole ratio of beryllium to oxygen in the following equation is:
$$Be + O_2 → BeO$$

A. 2/1.   C. 1.5/1.
B. 1/2.   D. 1/1.5.

34) TYPE: M   LEVEL: 2   TEXT REFERENCE: 6-3
ANSWER: D

The mass ratio of strontium to iodine in the following equation is:
$$175.2 \text{ g Sr} + 253.8 \text{ g I} → 429 \text{ g SrI}$$

A. 1/2.   C. 1/0.69.
B. 2/1.   D. 0.69/1.

35) TYPE: M   LEVEL: 2   TEXT REFERENCE: 6-3
ANSWER: D

Which of the following is a balanced equation that represents the
formation of water in terms of mass?

A. 2 mol H + 1 mol O → 2 mol H_2O
B. 2 mol H + 1 mol O → 1 mol H_2O
C. 1 g H + 16 g O → 17 g H_2O
D. 2 g H + 16 g O → 18 g H_2O

36) TYPE: M   LEVEL: 2   TEXT REFERENCE: 6-3
ANSWER: A

Which term completes the following balanced equation?
        27.6 g Li + 32 g O_2 → _____

A. 59.6 g Li_2O C. 29.8 g Li_2O
B. 18.2 g Li_2O D. 59.6 g Li_2O

37) TYPE: M   LEVEL: 1   TEXT REFERENCE: 6-4
ANSWER: C

Stoichiometry is used to determine:

A. the mole ratio.
B. the type of substances to be used.
C. the amount of substances to be used.
D. the molar concentration.

38) TYPE: M   LEVEL: 2   TEXT REFERENCE: 6-5
ANSWER: D

How many moles of potassium metal would be needed to react with
fluorine gas to make 400 g of KF?

A. 23 240.0 mol   C. 11620 mol
B. 13.76 mol   D. 6.88 mol

39) TYPE: M   LEVEL: 2   TEXT REFERENCE: 6-5
ANSWER: B

How many moles of hydrogen are needed to react with oxygen gas to
make 72 g of water?

A. 8 mol   C. 36 mol
B. 4 mol   D. 2 mol

40) TYPE: M   LEVEL: 2   TEXT REFERENCE: 6-5
ANSWER: A

How many grams of $NaClO_3$ must be decomposed to form sodium chloride
and 2.5 moles of oxygen?

A. 177.2 g   C. 70.8 g
B. 212.6 g   D. 123.8 g

41) TYPE: M   LEVEL: 2   TEXT REFERENCE: 6-6
ANSWER: A

How many grams of K are needed to produce 14 g of KOH in the reaction
$K + H_2O \rightarrow KOH + H_2$?

A. 9.75 g   C. 20.1 g
B. 0.69 g   D. 1.4 g

42) TYPE: M   LEVEL: 2   TEXT REFERENCE: 6-6
ANSWER: C

How many grams of sodium chloride are produced from decomposing of
354.4 grams of $NaClO_3$?

A. 19.44 g   C. 194.4 g
B. 1.09 g   D. 646.2 g

43) TYPE: M   LEVEL: 2   TEXT REFERENCE: 6-6
ANSWER: D

How many grams of oxygen will be required to react completely with
16.5 grams of potassium to form K_2O?

A. 0.2 g   C. 6.75 g
B. 13.5 g   D. 3.37 g

44) TYPE: M   LEVEL: 2   TEXT REFERENCE: 6-7
ANSWER: D

How many grams of nickel will react to replace silver in 300 mL of a
0.1M solution of $AgNO_3$ in the equation
       $Ni + 2AgNO_3 \rightarrow Ni(NO_3)_2 + 2Ag$?

A. 150 g   C. 29.35 g
B. 58.7 g   D. 0.88 g

45) TYPE: M   LEVEL: 2   TEXT REFERENCE: 6-7
ANSWER: A

How many grams of copper will react to replace silver in 300 mL of
0.100M solution of $AgNO_3$?

A. 0.95 g Cu   C. 1896 g Cu
B. 0.095 g Cu   D. 952.5 g Cu

46) TYPE: M   LEVEL: 2   TEXT REFERENCE: 6-8
ANSWER: A

In the following equation, which is the limiting reactant if 2.6 mol
of gold are reacted with 5.6 mol of HCl?
$$Au + 2HCl \rightarrow AuCl_2 + H_2$$

A. Au   C. H
B. HCl   D. Cl

47) TYPE: M   LEVEL: 2   TEXT REFERENCE: 6-8
ANSWER: B

In the following equation, which reactant is in excess if 3.2 moles
of copper are reacted with 6.6 moles of HCl?
$$Cu + 2HCl \rightarrow CuCl_2 + H_2$$

A. Cu   C. $CuCl_2$
B. HCl   D. H_2

48) TYPE: M   LEVEL: 3   TEXT REFERENCE: 6-9
ANSWER: A

What is the theoretical yield of NaCl if 53 g of Na_2CO_3 are
reacted with an excess of HCl?
$$Na_2CO_3 + 2HCl \rightarrow 2NaCl + H_2O + CO_2$$

A. 58.5 g   C. 85.3 g
B. 36.4 g   D. 68.0 g

49) TYPE: M   LEVEL: 3   TEXT REFERENCE: 6-9
ANSWER: B

What is the percent yield of water in a reaction in which the
theoretical yield was 45.42 g H_2O and the actual yield was only
36.25 g H_2O?

A. 6.17%   C. 125.2%
B. 79.8%   D. 12.5%

50) TYPE: M   LEVEL: 3   TEXT REFERENCE: 6-9
ANSWER: B

If a chemical reaction generates a high amount of waste or heat, the
percent yield will be:

A. relatively high.
B. relatively low.
C. the same as if there was no waste.
D. cannot tell.

Chapter 6   CALCULATIONS INVOLVING REACTIONS

51) TYPE: M   LEVEL: 4   TEXT REFERENCE: LA
ANSWER: A

What is the balanced equation for the reaction between hydrochloric acid and sodium hydrogen carbonate?

A. $NaHCO_3 + HCl \rightarrow NaCl + H_2O + CO_2$
B. $HCO_3 + Cl \rightarrow Cl + H_2O + CO_2$
C. $2NaHCO_2 + HCl \rightarrow 2NaCl + 2H_2O + CO_2$
D. $NaHCO + HCl \rightarrow NaCl + H_2O + CO$

52) TYPE: M   LEVEL: 4   TEXT REFERENCE: LB
ANSWER: B

In a reaction between solutions of calcium chloride and sodium carbonate, what procedure is followed to determine the mass of the product produced?

A. The sodium chloride precipitate is collected and dried.
B. The calcium carbonate precipitate is collected and dried.
C. The mass of dissolved sodium chloride is calculated.
D. the mass of dissolved calcium carbonate is calculated.

53) TYPE: M   LEVEL: 4   TEXT REFERENCE: LB
ANSWER: D

What volume of 0.004M calcium chloride solution would be required to completely react with 80.0 mL of 0.005M sodium carbonate solution?

A. 0.001 mL
B. 0.1 mL
C. 1 mL
D. 100 mL

54) TYPE: M   LEVEL: 4   TEXT REFERENCE: LC
ANSWER: C

What is the balanced equation for the reaction of sodium carbonate with hydrochloric acid?

A. $Na_2CO_3 + HCl \rightarrow NaCl + CO_2$
B. $Na_2CO_3 + 2HCl \rightarrow NaCl + H_2O + CO_2$
C. $Na_2CO_3 + 2HCl \rightarrow 2NaCl + H_2O + CO_2$
D. $Na_2CO_3 + 2HCl \rightarrow 2NaCl + CO_2$

55) TYPE: M   LEVEL: 4   TEXT REFERENCE: LC
ANSWER: A

How many milliliters of 1.00M HCl are required to make 0.415 mol of HCl?

A. 415 mL HCl
B. 41.5 mL HCl
C. 4.15 mL HCl
D. 0.415 mL HCl

56) TYPE: M   LEVEL: 4   TEXT REFERENCE: LD
ANSWER: C

If you have 3.45 g of zinc, how many moles do you have?

A. 65.4 mol
B. 3.45 mol

C. 0.053 mol
D. 225 mol

57) TYPE: M   LEVEL: 4   TEXT REFERENCE: LD
ANSWER: C

How many moles of HCl are required to react with 0.311 moles of zinc?

A. 2
B. 0.311

C. 0.622
D. 0.155

58) TYPE: M   LEVEL: 4   TEXT REFERENCE: LD
ANSWER: A

If a small amount of zinc remains at the conclusion of a reaction between zinc and hydrochloric acid, which reactant is in excess?

A. zinc
B. neither

C. hydrochloric acid
D. cannot tell

59) TYPE: M   LEVEL: 4   TEXT REFERENCE: LE
ANSWER: D

Which of the following errors may cause the experimental value for the mass of zinc to be smaller than the predicted mass?

A. The HCl was measured incorrectly.
B. Some zinc evaporated when the test tube was dried.
C. The concentration of HCl was greater than was predicted.
D. all of the above.

60) TYPE: M   LEVEL: 4   TEXT REFERENCE: LE
ANSWER: C

Which of the following experimental values is within experimental uncertainty of the calculated value 2.10g of zinc?

A. 2.01 g
B. 2.00 g

C. 2.12 g
D. both A and B

Chapter 7 GASES

1) TYPE: T   LEVEL: 1   TEXT REFERENCE: 7-1
ANSWER: F

_____ A solid is very sensitive to changes in temperature and
       pressure.

2) TYPE: T   LEVEL: 1   TEXT REFERENCE: 7-2
ANSWER: F

_____ Weight is the same as mass.

3) TYPE: T   LEVEL: 1   TEXT REFERENCE: 7-2
ANSWER: F

_____ Pressure is the same as force.

4) TYPE: T   LEVEL: 1   TEXT REFERENCE: 7-3
ANSWER: F

_____ A vacuum exerts a force inside a barometer equal to atmospheric
       pressure at sea level.

5) TYPE: T   LEVEL: 1   TEXT REFERENCE: 7-3
ANSWER: T

_____ The average pressure at sea level is called standard pressure.

6) TYPE: T   LEVEL: 1   TEXT REFERENCE: 7-4
ANSWER: F

_____ The partial pressure is the amount of pressure a gas exerts on
       the walls of a container divided by the pressure of other gases
       in the container.

7) TYPE: T   LEVEL: 1   TEXT REFERENCE: 7-5
ANSWER: T

_____ In order to convert a Celsius temperature to kelvins you must
       add 273.

8) TYPE: T   LEVEL: 1   TEXT REFERENCE: 7-6
ANSWER: F

_____ Boyle's law recognizes that the volume of a gas is directly
       proportional to the pressure applied to the gas.

9) TYPE: T   LEVEL: 1   TEXT REFERENCE: 7-8
ANSWER: F

_____   For most gas systems that are not under controlled laboratory
conditions, temperature changes usually accompany changes in
pressure.

10) TYPE: T   LEVEL: 1   TEXT REFERENCE: 7-9
ANSWER: T

_____   The kinetic molecular theory includes four sets of conditions
for an ideal gas.

11) TYPE: T   LEVEL: 1   TEXT REFERENCE: 7-9
ANSWER: F

_____   The sum of the distances traveled by the molecules of a gas
is known as the mean free path.

12) TYPE: T   LEVEL: 2   TEXT REFERENCE: 7-10
ANSWER: F

_____   The ideal gas law is a combination of Boyle's law and Charles's
law.

13) TYPE: T   LEVEL: 1   TEXT REFERENCE: 7-11
ANSWER: T

_____   Standard molar volume is a value for the space that one mole of
gas occupies at STP.

14) TYPE: T   LEVEL: 1   TEXT REFERENCE: 7-12
ANSWER: F

_____   Maxwell and Boltzmann found that the average velocity of a gas
molecule is inversely proportional to the temperature of the
gas.

15) TYPE: T   LEVEL: 1   TEXT REFERENCE: 7-13
ANSWER: T

_____   Graham's law can be used to find the molar mass of an unknown
gas.

16) TYPE: O   LEVEL: 1   TEXT REFERENCE: 7-1
ANSWER: solid

A _____ is a rigid state of matter with its own
shape.

17) TYPE: 0   LEVEL: 1   TEXT REFERENCE: 7-1
ANSWER: liquid

A _____ is a state of matter that takes the shape of
its container and whose volume is changed little by changes in
temperature or pressure.

18) TYPE: 0   LEVEL: 1   TEXT REFERENCE: 7-1
ANSWER: gas

A _____ is a state of matter that is very sensitive
to temperature and pressure changes.

19) TYPE: 0   LEVEL: 1   TEXT REFERENCE: 7-1
ANSWER: fluid

When molecules in a substance move freely past one another and
constantly change their relative positions, the substance is said to
be a _____ .

20) TYPE: 0   LEVEL: 1   TEXT REFERENCE: 7-2
ANSWER: weight

The force that gravity exerts on an object is its _____ .

21) TYPE: 0   LEVEL: 1   TEXT REFERENCE: 7-2
ANSWER: area

Pressure is measured in terms of force per unit of _____ .

22) TYPE: 0   LEVEL: 1   TEXT REFERENCE: 7-3
ANSWER: vacuum

A space in which the pressure is 0 Pa is called a(n)
_____ .

23) TYPE: 0   LEVEL: 1   TEXT REFERENCE: 7-3
ANSWER: barometer

A device used to measure the atmospheric pressure is called a(n)
_____ .

24) TYPE: 0   LEVEL: 1   TEXT REFERENCE: 7-4
ANSWER: total

Dalton's law of partial pressure may be expressed in the form of
$P_t = P_a + P_b \ldots P_z$, where P_t stands for
_____ pressure.

25) TYPE: O   LEVEL: 1   TEXT REFERENCE: 7-5
ANSWER: volume

Charles's law describes a situation in which the pressure and number of moles of a gas are constant, and the _____ is directly proportional to the temperature.

26) TYPE: O   LEVEL: 1   TEXT REFERENCE: 7-5
ANSWER: increases

The term direct proportion means that as one variable increases the other variable _____.

27) TYPE: O   LEVEL: 2   TEXT REFERENCE: 7-5
ANSWER: 231

A temperature of negative 42 degrees Celsius equals _____ kelvins.

28) TYPE: O   LEVEL: 1   TEXT REFERENCE: 7-6
ANSWER: inverse

Boyle's law recognizes a(n) _____ proportion between volume and pressure.

29) TYPE: O   LEVEL: 1   TEXT REFERENCE: 7-9
ANSWER: kinetic

The theory that describes the behavior of an ideal gas is the _____ molecular theory.

30) TYPE: O   LEVEL: 1   TEXT REFERENCE: 7-9
ANSWER: absolute

The lowest possible temperature is known as _____ zero.

31) TYPE: O   LEVEL: 1   TEXT REFERENCE: 7-10
ANSWER: constant

In the ideal gas law, the symbol R stands for a(n) _____.

32) TYPE: O   LEVEL: 1   TEXT REFERENCE: 7-13
ANSWER: diffuse

The subject of Graham's law is the rate at which gases _____.

33) TYPE: M   LEVEL: 1   TEXT REFERENCE: 7-1
ANSWER: B

What is not true about a gas?

A. Gases are fluids.
B. Without a container, gases maintain a constant shape.
C. Gases completely fill their containers.
D. Gas molecules are very sensitive to changes in pressure.

34) TYPE: M   LEVEL: 2   TEXT REFERENCE: 7-1
ANSWER: D

The molecules in a fluid are:

A. farther apart than molecules in a gas.
B. closer together than molecules in a solid.
C. closer together than molecules in a liquid.
D. free to move over, under, and around each other.

35) TYPE: M   LEVEL: 1   TEXT REFERENCE: 7-3
ANSWER: D

The letters STP stand for:

A. solid, time, and pressure.
B. solid, temperature, and pressure.
C. standard time and pressure.
D. standard temperature and pressure.

36) TYPE: M   LEVEL: 1   TEXT REFERENCE: 7-3
ANSWER: C

Pressure is not measured in:

A. atmosphere.   C. STP's.
B. kilopascals.   D. kPa's.

37) TYPE: M   LEVEL: 1   TEXT REFERENCE: 7-3
ANSWER: A

A device that can measure the pressure of any gas is a(n):

A. manometer.   C. vacuum.
B. barometer.   D. kelvin scale.

38) TYPE: M   LEVEL: 2   TEXT REFERENCE: 7-4
ANSWER: A

If total gas pressure is 99.2 k Pa, and the water vapor pressure is
2.6 k Pa, what is the partial pressure of nitrogen gas collected over
water?

A. 96.6 kPa   C. 96.6 atm
B. 101.8 kPa   D. 38.1 kPa

39) TYPE: M   LEVEL: 2   TEXT REFERENCE: 7-5
ANSWER: A

The temperature 78 degrees Celsius equals:

A. 351 degrees kelvin.   C. 531 kelvins.
B. 195 degrees kelvin.   D. 195 kelvins.

40) TYPE: M   LEVEL: 2   TEXT REFERENCE: 7-5
ANSWER: A

What must be kept constant for Charles's law to hold true?

A. pressure and number of moles
B. pressure and volume
C. temperature and pressure
D. temperature and number of moles

41) TYPE: M   LEVEL: 1   TEXT REFERENCE: 7-6
ANSWER: D

For a gas with temperature and number of moles held constant, Boyle's
law describes a situation in which:

A. volume and pressure have no relationship.
B. volume increases with increasing pressure.
C. volume decreases with decreasing speed.
D. volume decreases with increasing pressure.

42) TYPE: M   LEVEL: 2   TEXT REFERENCE: 7-8
ANSWER: A

A sample of oxygen gas has a volume of 7.84 cm³ at a pressure of
71.8 kPa and a temperature of 25 degrees Celsius. If the pressure
changes to 35.9 cm³ and the temperature falls to zero degrees
Celsius, the new volume is:
A. 14.4 cm³.   C. 17.1 cm³.
B. 15.7 cm³.   D. 3.92 cm³.

43) TYPE: M   LEVEL: 2   TEXT REFERENCE: 7-8
ANSWER: B

The volume of a sample of gas is 100 mL at 300 K and 49.1 kPa. What will be the volume of the gas at 350 K and 65.2 kPa?

A. 64.5 mL   C. 116.6 mL
B. 87.9 mL   D. 1.54 mL

44) TYPE: M   LEVEL: 1   TEXT REFERENCE: 7-9
ANSWER: D

Which of the following is not a condition of the kinetic molecular theory?

A. Gas molecules travel in a straight line.
B. Gas molecules in an ideal gas have no volume.
C. Gas molecules do not exert attractive forces.
D. The collisions that occur between gas molecules are perfectly inelastic.

45) TYPE: M   LEVEL: 1   TEXT REFERENCE: 7-10
ANSWER: D

The equation PV = k represents:

A. the ideal gas law.
B. Charles's law.
C. the kinetic molecular theory.
D. Boyle's law.

46) TYPE: M   LEVEL: 2   TEXT REFERENCE: 7-10
ANSWER: D

What is the pressure of 2.6 g of helium gas at 20 degrees Celsius that occupies 3.5 L?

A. 58.6 kPa   C. 54.4 kPa
B. 1025.5 kPa   D. 452.2 kPa

47) TYPE: M   LEVEL: 2   TEXT REFERENCE: 7-10
ANSWER: A

What is the pressure, in atm, of 3.0 g of helium gas at 20 degrees Celsius that occupies 4.0 L?

A. 4.5 atm   C. 3246.4 atm
B. 8.0 atm   D. 18.0 atm

48) TYPE: M   LEVEL: 1   TEXT REFERENCE: 7-11
ANSWER: D

Standard molar volume is:

A. 22.4 dm³.   C. 0.0821 dm³.
B. 0.0821 STP.   D. 22.4 dm³ at STP.

49) TYPE: M   LEVEL: 1   TEXT REFERENCE: 7-12
ANSWER: C

Kinetic energy is the energy of a particle due to its:

A. size.   C. motion.
B. charge.   D. direction.

50) TYPE: M   LEVEL: 1   TEXT REFERENCE: 7-13
ANSWER: B

Graham's law is based on the observation that the average kinetic
energies of any two gases are:

A. different at different temperatures.
B. equal at the same temperature.
C. equal at different temperatures.
D. different at the same temperature.

51) TYPE: M   LEVEL: 2   TEXT REFERENCE: 7-14
ANSWER: C

How many dm³ of water vapor are produced when 8 dm³ of hydrogen
gas reacts completely with 4 dm³ of oxygen gas?

A. 2 dm³   C. 8 dm³
B. 4 dm³   D. 32 dm³

52) TYPE: M   LEVEL: 2   TEXT REFERENCE: 7-14
ANSWER: D

When NaCl decomposes, how many grams of NaCl are needed to produce
0.9 L of Cl_2 measured at STP?

A. 0.9 g   C. 58.5 g
B. 52.2 g   D. 4.7 g

53) TYPE: M   LEVEL: 4   TEXT REFERENCE: LA
ANSWER: B

The graph of pressure versus volume for a contained gas (at constant
temperature) will show that:

A. as the pressure increases, the volume increases.
B. as the pressure increases, the volume decreases.
C. as the volume decreases, the pressure decreases.
D. none of the above.

54) TYPE: M   LEVEL: 4   TEXT REFERENCE: LA
ANSWER: A

The graph of temperature versus volume for a contained gas (at
constant pressure) shows what type of a proportion?

A. direct   C. both direct and inverse
B. inverse   D. cannot tell

55) TYPE: M   LEVEL: 4   TEXT REFERENCE: LB
ANSWER: D

The balanced equation for the single displacement reaction between
magnesium and hydrochloric acid is:

A. $Mg(s) + HCl (aq) \rightarrow H(g) + MgCl(aq)$
B. $Mg(s) + HCl(aq) \rightarrow H_2(g) + MgCl_2(aq)$
C. $2Mg(s) + 2HCL(aq) \rightarrow H_2(g) + MgCl_2(aq)$
D. $Mg(s) + 2HCl(aq) \rightarrow H_2(g) + MgCl_2(aq)$

56) TYPE: M   LEVEL: 4   TEXT REFERENCE: LB
ANSWER: A

The single displacement reaction between Mg and HCl involves:

A. the same number of moles of Mg as H_2.
B. the same number of moles of Mg as HCl.
C. twice as many moles of Mg as H_2.
D. twice as many moles of H_2 as Mg.

57) TYPE: M   LEVEL: 4   TEXT REFERENCE: LB
ANSWER: D

What volume would one mole of any gas occupy at 404.4 kPa and 100
degrees Celsius?

A. 8.2 L   C. 61.2 L
B. 13.3 L   D. 7.7 L

58) TYPE: M   LEVEL: 4   TEXT REFERENCE: LB
ANSWER: C

In the single replacement reaction between HCl and Mg, an increase in
the molarity of the HCl will:

A. decrease the final volume of H_2.
B. increase the final volume of H_2.
C. not affect the final volume of H_2.
D. decrease the molarity of Mg.

Chapter 8   COMPOSITION OF THE ATOM

1)   TYPE: T   LEVEL: 1   TEXT REFERENCE: 8-1
ANSWER: T

____   Models of atoms are based on scientific discoveries.

2)   TYPE: T   LEVEL: 1   TEXT REFERENCE: 8-1
ANSWER: F

____   John Dalton based his atomic model on the electrical nature
       of the atom, not on its chemical properties.

3)   TYPE: T   LEVEL: 1   TEXT REFERENCE: 8-2
ANSWER: F

____   A negative electrode in a cathode-ray tube is called an anode,
       while a positive electrode is called a cathode.

4)   TYPE: T   LEVEL: 1   TEXT REFERENCE: 8-2
ANSWER: T

____   J.J. Thomson found that the particles composing cathode rays
       were the same no matter what gas was in the tube.

5)   TYPE: T   LEVEL: 2   TEXT REFERENCE: 8-3
ANSWER: F

____   Atoms contain either negative particles or positive particles.

6)   TYPE: T   LEVEL: 3   TEXT REFERENCE: 8-4
ANSWER: T

____   In Thomson's experiments the e/m values for electrons were the
       same for all gases tested, while the values for the positive
       particles varied.

7)   TYPE: T   LEVEL: 1   TEXT REFERENCE: 8-6
ANSWER: F

____   Radioactive substances emit very penetrating rays called X
       rays.

8)   TYPE: T   LEVEL: 1   TEXT REFERENCE: 8-6
ANSWER: F

____   A gamma ray is a very penetrating beam of particles.

9) TYPE: T   LEVEL: 1   TEXT REFERENCE: 8-8
ANSWER: F

_____   The mass of a neutron is much larger than the mass of a
         proton.

10) TYPE: T   LEVEL: 1   TEXT REFERENCE: 8-9
ANSWER: F

_____   All atoms of the same element have the same mass.

11) TYPE: T   LEVEL: 1   TEXT REFERENCE: 8-9
ANSWER: T

_____   The atomic number defines an element.

12) TYPE: T   LEVEL: 1   TEXT REFERENCE: 8-9
ANSWER: F

_____   In the periodic table, the elements are listed in order of
         decreasing positive nuclear charge.

13) TYPE: T   LEVEL: 1   TEXT REFERENCE: 8-10
ANSWER: F

_____   Atoms of the same element with different numbers of electrons
         are called isotopes.

14) TYPE: T   LEVEL: 1   TEXT REFERENCE: 8-10
ANSWER: T

_____   The stability of an isotope depends on the number of neutrons
         relative to the number of protons in the atoms of that isotope.

15) TYPE: T   LEVEL: 1   TEXT REFERENCE: 8-10
ANSWER: F

_____   In the periodic table, the atomic masses will always be whole
         numbers.

16) TYPE: O   LEVEL: 1   TEXT REFERENCE: 8-2
ANSWER: electrodes

Conductors used to establish electrical contact are called
_____.

17) TYPE: 0   LEVEL: 1   TEXT REFERENCE: 8-2
ANSWER: anode

In a cathode-ray tube, a positive electrode is called a(n)
_____.

18) TYPE: 0   LEVEL: 1   TEXT REFERENCE: 8-2
ANSWER: cathode

A tube that emits a beam originating from the negative electrode is
known as a(n) _____-ray tube.

19) TYPE: 0   LEVEL: 1   TEXT REFERENCE: 8-3
ANSWER: proton

The positive particle in an atom is known as a(n) _____.

20) TYPE: 0   LEVEL: 2   TEXT REFERENCE: 8-3
ANSWER: energy

The equation for the ionization of a chlorine atom is:
$$Cl + \underline{\hspace{3cm}} \rightarrow Cl^- + e^-$$

21) TYPE: 0   LEVEL: 3   TEXT REFERENCE: 8-4
ANSWER: charge-to-mass ratio

A value first calculated by Thomson that describes the electron is
the _____.

22) TYPE: 0   LEVEL: 3   TEXT REFERENCE: 8-4
ANSWER: charge

The e in the e/m ratio stands for the size of the _____.

23) TYPE: 0   LEVEL: 1   TEXT REFERENCE: 8-5
ANSWER: subatomic

Charged particles known as electrons and protons that make up an atom
are called _____ particles.

24) TYPE: 0   LEVEL: 1   TEXT REFERENCE: 8-6
ANSWER: radioactivity

The spontaneous disintegration of certain atoms evidenced by the
emission of particles and/or energy beams is known as
_____.

25) TYPE: O   LEVEL: 1   TEXT REFERENCE: 8-6
ANSWER: beta

High-speed electrons emitted from radioactive nuclei are called
_____ particles.

26) TYPE: O   LEVEL: 1   TEXT REFERENCE: 8-6
ANSWER: alpha

In 1909, Ernest Rutherford devised an experiment to locate the source
of _____ particles in the atoms of radioactive
substances.

27) TYPE: O   LEVEL: 1   TEXT REFERENCE: 8-7
ANSWER: nucleus

The center of an atom is the _____.

28) TYPE: O   LEVEL: 1   TEXT REFERENCE: 8-8
ANSWER: neutrons

Uncharged particles with about the same mass as protons are known as
_____.

29) TYPE: O   LEVEL: 2   TEXT REFERENCE: 8-9
ANSWER: neutrons

The difference between the mass number and the atomic number of an
isotope is equal to the number of _____.

30) TYPE: O   LEVEL: 1   TEXT REFERENCE: 8-9
ANSWER: protons

Elements differ from one another according to the number of
_____ found in the nucleus of the atoms.

31) TYPE: O   LEVEL: 1   TEXT REFERENCE: 8-9
ANSWER: ion

If an atom loses or gains electrons, it becomes a(n) _____.

32) TYPE: O   LEVEL: 1   TEXT REFERENCE: 8-9
ANSWER: protons

The atomic number of an element is the number of _____
in the nucleus of the atoms.

33) TYPE: O   LEVEL: 2   TEXT REFERENCE: 8-9
ANSWER: 20

There are _____ neutrons present in an atom of potassium, which has a mass number of 39 and an atomic number of 19.

34) TYPE: O   LEVEL: 1   TEXT REFERENCE: 8-10
ANSWER: isotopes

Atoms of the same element with different numbers of neutrons are called _____.

35) TYPE: O   LEVEL: 1   TEXT REFERENCE: 8-10
ANSWER: smaller

The mass of an electron is _____ than the mass of an atom.

36) TYPE: O   LEVEL: 3   TEXT REFERENCE: 8-11
ANSWER: spectrometer

A tool that can be used to determine the relative abundance of each isotope of an element is called the mass _____.

37) TYPE: O   LEVEL: 1   TEXT REFERENCE: 8-2
ANSWER: D

The negatively charged particles that Thomson studied were later identified as:

A. protons.   C. beta particles.
B. alpha particles.   D. electrons.

38) TYPE: O   LEVEL: 2   TEXT REFERENCE: 8-3
ANSWER: D

Which of the following is a balanced equation that expresses the ionization of a Krypton atom into its positive ion?

A. $Kr_2 \rightarrow Kr^+$
B. $Kr_2 + energy \rightarrow Kr^+$
C. $Kr_2 + energy \rightarrow Kr^+ + e^-$
D. $Kr + energy \rightarrow Kr^+ + e^-$

39) TYPE: O   LEVEL: 3   TEXT REFERENCE: 8-4
ANSWER: D

By using the e/m ratios for a hydrogen ion and an electron, Thomson found that compared to that of the ion:

A. the charge of the electron is large.
B. the mass of the electron is large.
C. the charge of the electron is small.
D. the mass of the electron is small.

40) TYPE: O   LEVEL: 3   TEXT REFERENCE: 8-4
ANSWER: B

The e/m value Thomson obtained for the hydrogen ion was larger than for any other positive ion, so he concluded that:

A. the mass of the hydrogen atom was the largest
B. the mass of the hydrogen atom was the smallest.
C. the charge was larger than the charge of the electron.
D. the charge was smaller than the charge on the electron.

41) TYPE: M   LEVEL: 1   TEXT REFERENCE: 8-6
ANSWER: A

High-speed particles with masses equal to those of helium nuclei are:

A. alpha particles.   C. gamma rays.
B. beta particles.   D. subatomic particles.

42) TYPE: M   LEVEL: 1   TEXT REFERENCE: 8-6
ANSWER: C

Gamma rays:

A. are beams of high-speed particles.
B. are beams of high-speed electrons.
C. are beams of high-energy rays.
D. have a mass equal to that of alpha particles.

43) TYPE: M   LEVEL: 1   TEXT REFERENCE: 8-7
ANSWER: C

The nucleus of an atom has what type of charge?

A. no charge   C. positive charge
B. slightly negative charge D. large negative charge

Chapter 8   COMPOSITION OF THE ATOM

44) TYPE: M   LEVEL: 1   TEXT REFERENCE: 8-9
ANSWER: B

A particle in the center of an atom whose charge is equal and
opposite to the charge of an electron is a(n):

A. neutron.   C. alpha particle.
B. proton.   D. beta particle.

45) TYPE: M   LEVEL: 1   TEXT REFERENCE: 8-9
ANSWER: D

The mass of an atom is determined by its:

A. protons and electrons.   C. protons only.
B. neutrons and electrons.   D. protons and neutrons.

46) TYPE: M   LEVEL: 2   TEXT REFERENCE: 8-9
ANSWER: C

In an atom with no charge:

A. there are more neutrons than electrons.
B. there are equal numbers of neutrons and electrons.
C. there are equal numbers of protons and electrons.
D. there are more neutrons than protons.

47) TYPE: M   LEVEL: 2   TEXT REFERENCE: 8-9
ANSWER: C

The number of electrons in a neutral atom is equal to the:

A. mass number.
B. number of protons and neutrons.
C. number of protons.
D. number of neutrons

48) TYPE: M   LEVEL: 2   TEXT REFERENCE: 8-9
ANSWER: B

How many neutrons are present in an atom of fluorine, which has a mass
number of 19 and an atomic number of 9?

A. 19   C. 9
B. 10   D. 28

49) TYPE: M   LEVEL: 2   TEXT REFERENCE: 8-9
ANSWER: C

A neutral atom with 34 neutrons and 16 electrons has a mass number of:

A. 18.   C. 50.
B. 52.   D. 68.

50) TYPE: M   LEVEL: 1   TEXT REFERENCE: 8-10
ANSWER: C

Atoms of isotopes of the same element differ in their:

A. number of electrons.
B. number of protons.
C. number of neutrons.
D. number of both neutrons and electrons.

51) TYPE: M   LEVEL: 2   TEXT REFERENCE: 8-10
ANSWER: B

What is the average atomic mass of boron, if in any sample of boron, 19.6% of the atoms have a mass of 10.0129 amu and 80.4% of the atoms have a mass of 11.0093?

A. 1087.0 amu   C. 687.2 amu
B. 10.81 amu   D. 17.75 amu

52) TYPE: M   LEVEL: 4   TEXT REFERENCE: LA
ANSWER: A

In an electroplating cell, the number of atoms being plated should be:

A. equal to the number being dissolved.
B. greater than the number being dissolved.
C. less than the number being dissolved.
D. cannot tell.

53) TYPE: M   LEVEL: 4   TEXT REFERENCE: LA
ANSWER: C

In an electroplating cell, the change in mass on the positive electrode should be:

A. greater than that on the negative electrode.
B. less than that on the negative electrode.
C. equal to that on the negative electrode.
D. one-half of that on the negative electrode.

54) TYPE: M   LEVEL: 4   TEXT REFERENCE: LA
ANSWER: A

In order to find the number of atoms involved at each electrode in an electroplating cell, you must:

A. divide the change in mass by the mass of one atom.
B. divide the mass of one atom by the change in mass.
C. divide the number of atoms plated by the change in mass.
D. multiply the change in mass by the mass of one atom.

55) TYPE: M   LEVEL: 4   TEXT REFERENCE: LA
ANSWER: B

In order to calculate the charge on one atom in an electroplating cell you must:

A. multiply total charge by number of atoms.
B. divide total charge by number of atoms.
C. divide total charge by mass of one atom.
D. multiply total charge by mass of one atom.

56) TYPE: M   LEVEL: 4   TEXT REFERENCE: LA
ANSWER: C

In order to calculate the elementary charge carried by one electron in a zinc electroplating cell you must:

A. divide the charge per atom by number of atoms.
B. multiply the charge per atom by number of atoms.
C. divide the charge per atom by two.
D. none of the above.

57) TYPE: M   LEVEL: 4   TEXT REFERENCE: LA
ANSWER: B

The elementary charge is expressed in terms of:

A. mass of one electron.
B. ampere-seconds per one electron.
C. amperes carried by one electron.
D. volts carried by one electron.

58) TYPE: M   LEVEL: 4   TEXT REFERENCE: LA
ANSWER: A

If the charge on one electron is 1.6×10^{-19} ampere-seconds and its mass is 9.1×10^{-28} grams, what is its charge-to-mass ratio?

A. 1.8×10^{8} ampere-seconds/g.
B. 1.8×10^{-8} ampere-seconds/g.
C. 5.7×10^{9} ampere-seconds/g.
D. 5.7×10^{-9} ampere-seconds/g.

Chapter 9 NUCLEAR CHEMISTRY

1) TYPE: T   LEVEL: 2   TEXT REFERENCE: 9-1
ANSWER: T

_____ Atoms of uranium-235 and uranium-238 have the same number of protons but different numbers of neutrons.

2) TYPE: T   LEVEL: 1   TEXT REFERENCE: 9-2
ANSWER: T

_____ Light, alpha particles, and heat are all forms of radiation.

3) TYPE: T   LEVEL: 1   TEXT REFERENCE: 9-2
ANSWER: F

_____ Beta particles have a charge that is the same as a proton.

4) TYPE: T   LEVEL: 1   TEXT REFERENCE: 9-2
ANSWER: F

_____ X rays and gamma rays are forms of nonionizing radiation.

5) TYPE: T   LEVEL: 2   TEXT REFERENCE: 9-3
ANSWER: F

_____ Gamma decay causes a decrease in both the atomic number and the mass number.

6) TYPE: T   LEVEL: 1   TEXT REFERENCE: 9-5
ANSWER: T

_____ Transuranium elements are synthesized elements with atomic numbers greater than 92.

7) TYPE: T   LEVEL: 3   TEXT REFERENCE: 9-6
ANSWER: T

_____ The cyclotron is less powerful than the synchrotron.

8) TYPE: T   LEVEL: 1   TEXT REFERENCE: 9-7
ANSWER: F

_____ Half-life is the time it takes for one-half of the protons in a radioactive sample to decay.

9) TYPE: T   LEVEL: 1   TEXT REFERENCE: 9-8
ANSWER: T

____   PET and SPECT are tools used by doctors to diagnose organ
       malfunctions.

10) TYPE: T   LEVEL: 1   TEXT REFERENCE: 9-9
ANSWER: F

____   The c in the equation $E = mc^2$ is the velocity of sound.

11) TYPE: T   LEVEL: 1   TEXT REFERENCE: 9-10
ANSWER: T

____   Fission is an example of a chain reaction.

12) TYPE: T   LEVEL: 1   TEXT REFERENCE: 9-11
ANSWER: F

____   In a fission reactor, neutrons are slowed down by control rods.

13) TYPE: T   LEVEL: 1   TEXT REFERENCE: 9-12
ANSWER: T

____   A fission reaction produces less energy than a fusion reaction.

14) TYPE: T   LEVEL: 1   TEXT REFERENCE: 9-14
ANSWER: F

____   A quark is a theoretical particle with a charge opposite that
       of the original particle.

15) TYPE: O   LEVEL: 1   TEXT REFERENCE: 9-1
ANSWER: nuclide

Each isotope of an element is called a(n) _____.

16) TYPE: O   LEVEL: 1   TEXT REFERENCE: 9-2
ANSWER: radiation

A general term for particles or energy emitted from a source and
traveling through space is _____.

17) TYPE: O   LEVEL: 1   TEXT REFERENCE: 9-2
ANSWER: ionizing

Radiation that causes a change in matter is called _____
radiation.

18) TYPE: 0   LEVEL: 1   TEXT REFERENCE: 9-2
ANSWER: rem

A unit used to measure the amount of radiation absorbed by humans is
the _____.

19) TYPE: 0   LEVEL: 1   TEXT REFERENCE: 9-3
ANSWER: emission

The release of an alpha particle during radioactive decay is known as
alpha _____.

20) TYPE: 0   LEVEL: 1   TEXT REFERENCE: 9-3
ANSWER: parent

In a decay reaction, the initial element is called the
_____ nuclide.

21) TYPE: 0   LEVEL: 1   TEXT REFERENCE: 9-3
ANSWER: beta

The emission of an electron from an atomic nucleus is known as
_____ emission.

22) TYPE: 0   LEVEL: 2   TEXT REFERENCE: 9-3
ANSWER: alpha

A decrease in the mass number by four is a result of _____
decay.

23) TYPE: 0   LEVEL: 1   TEXT REFERENCE: 9-4
ANSWER: spontaneous

If the alpha and beta emissions of a nuclide occur naturally, the
process is known as _____ decay.

24) TYPE: 0   LEVEL: 1   TEXT REFERENCE: 9-5
ANSWER: transmutation

The process of changing one element into another is known as
_____.

25) TYPE: 0   LEVEL: 3   TEXT REFERENCE: 9-6
ANSWER: cyclotron

One of the earliest particle accelerators was the
_____.

26) **TYPE:** 0   **LEVEL:** 3   **TEXT REFERENCE:** 9-6
ANSWER: electromagnets

Particle accelerators make use of _____ to increase
the speeds of moving charged particles.

27) **TYPE:** 0   **LEVEL:** 1   **TEXT REFERENCE:** 9-7
ANSWER: disintegrations

Radioactivity can be measured in terms of the number of
_____ that occur per minute per gram.

28) **TYPE:** 0   **LEVEL:** 2   **TEXT REFERENCE:** 9-7
ANSWER: 5730

A living plant gives off 15.3 disintegrations/min/g of material
containing carbon-14, whose half-life is 5730 years. A piece of wood
that is giving off 7.65 dinistegrations per minute per gram is
_____ years old.

29) **TYPE:** 0   **LEVEL:** 1   **TEXT REFERENCE:** 9-8
ANSWER: tracer

A radioactive isotope used to keep track of what happens to a
chemical during a physical or chemical change is a(n) _____.

30) **TYPE:** 0   **LEVEL:** 1   **TEXT REFERENCE:** 9-9
ANSWER: energy

The mathematical equation $E = mc^2$, derived by Einstein, relates
_____ to mass.

31) **TYPE:** 0   **LEVEL:** 1   **TEXT REFERENCE:** 9-9
ANSWER: defect

The difference in mass between a nucleus and the total mass of the
particles composing it is known as the mass _____.

32) **TYPE:** 0   **LEVEL:** 1   **TEXT REFERENCE:** 9-10
ANSWER: chain

A self-propagating reaction is called a(n) _____
reaction.

33) TYPE: O   LEVEL: 1   TEXT REFERENCE: 9-11
ANSWER: moderator

Water molecules used to slow down neutrons in nuclear reactors are an
example of a(n) _____.

34) TYPE: O   LEVEL: 1   TEXT REFERENCE: 9-11
ANSWER: rods

Cadmium, which absorbs neutrons, is used in the form of _____
to control the rate of nuclear reactions.

35) TYPE: O   LEVEL: 1   TEXT REFERENCE: 9-12
ANSWER: fusion

A process known as _____ occurs when small nuclei join
to form larger nuclei.

36) TYPE: O   LEVEL: 3   TEXT REFERENCE: 9-13
ANSWER: vitrification

Radioactive wastes may be dissolved and stored in glass by a process
known as _____.

37) TYPE: O   LEVEL: 1   TEXT REFERENCE: 9-15
ANSWER: antimatter

The collective name given to particles that are opposites of
particles of matter is _____.

38) TYPE: M   LEVEL: 1   TEXT REFERENCE: 9-1
ANSWER: B

Which of the following is not true about two nuclides of the same
element?

A. They have the same number of electrons.
B. They have the same number of neutrons.
C. They have the same number of protons.
D. Their chemical nature is the same.

39) TYPE: M   LEVEL: 1   TEXT REFERENCE: 9-2
ANSWER: A

Which of the following is an example of nonionizing radiation?

A. visible light rays   C. gamma rays
B. X rays   D. nuclide rays

40) TYPE: M   LEVEL: 1   TEXT REFERENCE: 9-2
ANSWER: D

Oppositely charged particles formed from irradiated matter are called:

A. immature cells.   C. beta particles.
B. cancer cells.   D. ion pairs.

41) TYPE: M   LEVEL: 1   TEXT REFERENCE: 9-3
ANSWER: A

The source of radioactivity is:

A. an unstable atomic nucleus.
B. an atom with too many electrons.
C. gamma decay.
D. spontaneous decay.

42) TYPE: M   LEVEL: 1   TEXT REFERENCE: 9-3
ANSWER: C

In a nuclear decay reaction, the initial and resulting elements are called, respectively:

A. parent cell and daughter cell.
B. daughter nuclide and parent nuclide.
C. parent nuclide and daughter nuclide.
D. daughter and parent.

43) TYPE: M   LEVEL: 2   TEXT REFERENCE: 9-3
ANSWER: C

A type of radioactive decay that causes no change in the atomic number or mass number is:

A. alpha decay.   C. gamma decay.
B. beta decay.   D. spontaneous decay.

44) TYPE: M   LEVEL: 2   TEXT REFERENCE: 9-4
ANSWER: A

Bombarding one stable nucleus with other particles will not cause:

A. high levels of radiation.
B. emission of a beta particle.
C. a chargeless emmission.
D. nuclear reactions.

45) TYPE: M   LEVEL: 2   TEXT REFERENCE: 9-5
ANSWER: D

All of the transuranium elements that have so far been synthesized
are not:

A. produced by large amounts of energy.
B. radioactive.
C. decaying in alpha emission.
D. found in nature.

46) TYPE: M   LEVEL: 2   TEXT REFERENCE: 9-7
ANSWER: B

A tree that was living 5730 years ago (the half-life of carbon-14)
will presently have a rate of radioactivity in disintegrations/min/g
that is:

A. as large as C-14.
B. one-half as large as C-14.
C. one-quarter as large as C-14.
D. twice as large as C-14.

47) TYPE: M   LEVEL: 2   TEXT REFERENCE: 9-7
ANSWER: B

A living plant gives off 15.3 disintegrations/min/g of material
containing carbon-14, whose half-life is 5730 years. How old is a
piece of wood that is giving off 3.82 disintegrations per minute per
gram?

A. 5730 years   C. 17 190 years
B. 11 460 years   D. 2865 years

48) TYPE: M   LEVEL: 1   TEXT REFERENCE: 9-8
ANSWER: D

The choice of an isotope for a medical procedure depends on its:

A. dosage.   C. chemical activity.
B. half-life.   D. all of these.

49) TYPE: M   LEVEL: 1   TEXT REFERENCE: 9-8
ANSWER: A

The radioisotope iodine-131 can be used as a tracer for what target
organ?

A. thyroid gland   C. lymph glands
B. spleen   D. brain

50) TYPE: M   LEVEL: 1   TEXT REFERENCE: 9-9
ANSWER: D

The E in the equation $E = mc^2$ represents:

A. energy in kilopascals.   C. energy in pascals.
B. Einstein.   D. energy in joules.

51) TYPE: M   LEVEL: 2   TEXT REFERENCE: 9-9
ANSWER: D

Calculate the binding energy, in joules, for one nucleus of lead-125
if the mass of one mole of lead-125 is 1.75 grams. (The speed of
light is 3.00×10^8m.)

A. 1.575×10^{13} J   C. 2.62×10^{10} J
B. 1.575×10^{14} J   D. 2.62×10^{-10} J

52) TYPE: M   LEVEL: 1   TEXT REFERENCE: 9-10
ANSWER: B

The process in which a nucleus is broken into smaller nuclei by
bombardment with low-energy neutrons is known as:

A. fusion.   C. natural decay.
B. fission.   D. transmutation.

53) TYPE: M   LEVEL: 1   TEXT REFERENCE: 9-9
ANSWER: C

The energy needed to break a nucleus into its component particles is
the:

A. threshold energy.   C. binding energy.
B. half-life.   D. fission energy.

54) TYPE: M   LEVEL: 1   TEXT REFERENCE: 9-10
ANSWER: D

The minimum amount of material needed to keep a chain-reaction going
is called the:

A. self-propagating mass.   C. moderating mass.
B. parent nuclide.   D. critical mass.

55) TYPE: M   LEVEL: 2   TEXT REFERENCE: 9-11
ANSWER: B

As the control rods are lowered into the fuel-rod assembly of a
nuclear reactor, the:

A. rate of reaction speeds up.
B. rate of reaction slows down.
C. rate of reaction is not affected.
D. water becomes hotter.

56) TYPE: M   LEVEL: 3   TEXT REFERENCE: 9-13
ANSWER: C

Most of nuclear waste is composed of:

A. radioactive cooling   C. spent fuel rods.
   elements.
B. decayed elements.   D. spent moderators.

57) TYPE: M   LEVEL: 4   TEXT REFERENCE: LA
ANSWER: A

Alpha trajectories are shaped:

A. long and straight.   C. long and curved.
B. short and straight.   D. short and curved.

58) TYPE: M   LEVEL: 4   TEXT REFERENCE: LA
ANSWER: A

Which material--lead, cardboard, or aluminum--is most effective in
shielding radiation?

A. lead   C. cardboard
B. aluminum   D. all are the same

59) TYPE: M   LEVEL: 4   TEXT REFERENCE: LA
ANSWER: D

Radiocarbon dating is most effective in determining the age of:

A. objects containing carbon.
B. objects that do not contain carbon.
C. objects that originated in living organisms.
D. both A and C

60) TYPE: M   LEVEL: 4   TEXT REFERENCE: LA
ANSWER: D

A Geiger counter is used to detect the presence of:

A. alpha particles.   C. Geiger particles.
B. beta particles.   D. both A and B.

Chapter 10   ELECTRONS IN ATOMS

1) TYPE: T   LEVEL: 1   TEXT REFERENCE: 10-1
ANSWER: T

____   The model that Ernest Rutherford designed for the atom had to
        be revised because it did not account for the fact that atoms
        are stable.

2) TYPE: T   LEVEL: 1   TEXT REFERENCE: 10-3
ANSWER: F

____   The wavelengths of light are no longer than the wavelengths of
        water waves.

3) TYPE: T   LEVEL: 1   TEXT REFERENCE: 10-3
ANSWER: T

____   The energy of a photon is described by the equation $E = h\nu$.

4) TYPE: T   LEVEL: 3   TEXT REFERENCE: 10-4
ANSWER: T

____   In a vacuum, radio waves, X rays, and visible light all travel
        at the speed of light.

5) TYPE: T   LEVEL: 3   TEXT REFERENCE: 10-4
ANSWER: F

____   For any electromagnetic wave, the wavelength and frequency are
        directly proportional.

6) TYPE: T   LEVEL: 1   TEXT REFERENCE: 10-5
ANSWER: T

____   The bright-line spectrum for each element is unique.

7) TYPE: T   LEVEL: 1   TEXT REFERENCE: 10-6
ANSWER: F

____   Ionization energy is the energy that is needed to move an
        electron from one energy level to another without being removed
        from the atom.

8) TYPE: T   LEVEL: 1   TEXT REFERENCE: 10-7
ANSWER: F

____   The ground state occurs when an atom is in its highest energy
        state.

9) TYPE: T   LEVEL: 2   TEXT REFERENCE: 10-7
ANSWER: F

_____   In an imaginary, many-electron atom, each orbital in the
        tenth energy level would have the same amount of energy.

10) TYPE: T   LEVEL: 2   TEXT REFERENCE: 10-7
ANSWER: F

_____   The exact position and path of an electron in an atom can be
        determined by spectroscopy.

11) TYPE: T   LEVEL: 1   TEXT REFERENCE: 10-8
ANSWER: T

_____   The quantum number n refers to the size of an orbital.

12) TYPE: T   LEVEL: 3   TEXT REFERENCE: 10-9
ANSWER: F

_____   Dark lines in a continuous spectrum are caused by the emission
        of light at specific wavelengths.

13) TYPE: T   LEVEL: 3   TEXT REFERENCE: 10-9
ANSWER: T

_____   The bright-line spectrum of an element is also called the
        emission spectrum.

14) TYPE: T   LEVEL: 3   TEXT REFERENCE: 10-9
ANSWER: T

_____   The absorption spectrum for any element is unique.

15) TYPE: T   LEVEL: 2   TEXT REFERENCE: 10-10
ANSWER: T

_____   Two electrons can have the same first three quantum numbers.

16) TYPE: O   LEVEL: 1   TEXT REFERENCE: 10-2
ANSWER: frequency

The Hertz is a measure of _____.

17) TYPE: O   LEVEL: 1   TEXT REFERENCE: 10-3
ANSWER: continuous

White light projected through a narrow slit and then a prism produces
a(n) _____ spectrum.

18) TYPE: O   LEVEL: 1   TEXT REFERENCE: 10-3
ANSWER: photons

Light energy comes in quantized packets known as
_____.

19) TYPE: O   LEVEL: 1   TEXT REFERENCE: 10-3
ANSWER: zero

A node of a standing wave has an amplitude equal to
_____.

20) TYPE: O   LEVEL: 1   TEXT REFERENCE: 10-3
ANSWER: decreases

As the frequency of a standing wave increases, the wavelength
_____.

21) TYPE: O   LEVEL: 2   TEXT REFERENCE: 10-3
ANSWER: two

A standing wave with five nodes would have _____
wavelength(s).

22) TYPE: O   LEVEL: 3   TEXT REFERENCE: 10-4
ANSWER: wavelength

For an electromagnetic wave, the product of its frequency and its
_____ is equal to the velocity of light.

23) TYPE: O   LEVEL: 1   TEXT REFERENCE: 10-6
ANSWER: ionization

The amount of energy needed to remove an electron from a gaseous atom
is known as the _____ energy.

24) TYPE: O   LEVEL: 1   TEXT REFERENCE: 10-7
ANSWER: mechanics

The branch of physics that describes the behavior of electrons in
terms of quantized energy is called quantum _____.

25) TYPE: 0   LEVEL: 1   TEXT REFERENCE: 10-7
ANSWER: probability

The likelihood of an occurrence is called _____.

26) TYPE: 0   LEVEL: 1   TEXT REFERENCE: 10-7
ANSWER: orbital

The region of space around a nucleus in which an electron is most
likely to be found is called a(n) _____.

27) TYPE: 0   LEVEL: 2   TEXT REFERENCE: 10-7
ANSWER: three

For the third orbital in an atom, the principal quantum number is
_____.

28) TYPE: 0   LEVEL: 2   TEXT REFERENCE: 10-7
ANSWER: 1s.

A spherical orbital in the first energy level would be written
symbolically as _____.

29) TYPE: 0   LEVEL: 3   TEXT REFERENCE: 10-9
ANSWER: spectroscopy

The most powerful technique astronomers have for analyzing the
chemical composition of the stars is _____.

30) TYPE: 0   LEVEL: 1   TEXT REFERENCE: 10-10
ANSWER: exclusion

The Pauli _____ principle states that no two
electrons in the same atom can have the same four quantum numbers.

31) TYPE: 0   LEVEL: 1   TEXT REFERENCE: 10-11
ANSWER: configuration

The procedure of organizing electrons in a many-electron atom leads to
the electron _____ of the atom.

32) TYPE: M   LEVEL: 1   TEXT REFERENCE: 10-2
ANSWER: B

Which of the following is not used to describe frequency?

A. Hz   C. cycles per second
B. meters   D. hertz

33) TYPE: M   LEVEL: 1   TEXT REFERENCE: 10-2
ANSWER: A

The distance between two waves that is measured to find the
wavelength is the distance between:

A. crest and crest.
B. crest and trough.
C. an imaginary line and the crest.
D. an imaginary line and the trough.

34) TYPE: M   LEVEL: 2   TEXT REFERENCE: 10-2
ANSWER: C

The distance up or down that a buoy bobs in the ocean as waves pass
is described by which property of waves?

A. frequency   C. amplitude
B. wavelength   D. period

35) TYPE: M   LEVEL: 1   TEXT REFERENCE: 10-3
ANSWER: C

Each color of light has its own:

A. frequency.   C. frequency and wavelength.
B. wavelength.   D. meter.

36) TYPE: M   LEVEL: 1   TEXT REFERENCE: 10-3
ANSWER: C

The letter v in the equation $E = hv$ represents:

A. Planck's constant.   C. frequency.
B. 6.6262×10^{-34}.   D. amplitude.

37) TYPE: M   LEVEL: 2   TEXT REFERENCE: 10-3
ANSWER: D

A photon of red light has more energy than a photon of:

A. yellow light.
B. blue light.
C. either yellow light or blue light.
D. water.

38) TYPE: M   LEVEL: 3   TEXT REFERENCE: 10-4
ANSWER: C

Which of the following does not involve electromagnetic waves?

A. listening to the radio   C. floating in the ocean
B. having your teeth   D. shining a flashlight
   X-rayed

39) TYPE: M   LEVEL: 3   TEXT REFERENCE: 10-4
ANSWER: A

For any electromagnetic wave in a vacuum, the product of the
wavelength and frequency must be equal to:

A. 3.0×10^8 m/s.
B. 6.6262×10^{-32} J/s.
C. 10^{14} cycles per second.
D. 3.0×10^{-8} m/s.

40) TYPE: M   LEVEL: 1   TEXT REFERENCE: 10-6
ANSWER: B

The light energy given off by an "excited" atom is equal to the
energy:

A. gained as the atom returns to a lower level.
B. lost as the atom returns to a lower level.
C. gained as the atom returns to a higher level.
D. lost as the atom returns to a higher level.

41) TYPE: M   LEVEL: 1   TEXT REFERENCE: 10-6
ANSWER: C

The equation that represents the combination of hydrogen ions and
electrons to form neutral hydrogen atoms is:

A. $H + e \rightarrow H(g)$.
B. $H^+ + e^- \rightarrow H(g)$.
C. $H^+ + e^- \rightarrow H(g) + 1312$ kJ.
D. $H^+ + e^- + 1312$ kJ $\rightarrow H(g)$.

42) TYPE: M   LEVEL: 1   TEXT REFERENCE: 10-7
ANSWER: C

The number of orbitals for each energy level of an atom is:

A. the principal quantum number.
B. n.
C. n^2.
D. n-1.

43) TYPE: M   LEVEL: 1   TEXT REFERENCE: 10-7
ANSWER: A

The letter that designates the first orbital in an energy level is:

A. s.   C. n.
B. p.   D. P_x.

44) TYPE: M   LEVEL: 2   TEXT REFERENCE: 10-7
ANSWER: B

How many orbitals would the tenth energy level of an imaginary atom
contain?

A. 10   C. 1000
B. 100   D. 9

45) TYPE: M   LEVEL: 1   TEXT REFERENCE: 10-8
ANSWER: C

The quantum number m describes which characteristic?

A. the size of an orbital
B. the shape of an orbital
C. the orientation of an orbital around the axes
D. the spin of an electron

46) TYPE: M   LEVEL: 2   TEXT REFERENCE: 10-8
ANSWER: C

A double-lobed orbital of the third energy level oriented around the
y-axis would be written as:

A. $2p_y$.   C. $3p_y$.
B. $2d_y$.   D. $3d_y$.

47) TYPE: M   LEVEL: 3   TEXT REFERENCE: 10-9
ANSWER: B

About 96% of the composition of the stars is:

A. hydrogen.   C. helium.
B. hydrogen and helium.   D. neon and argon.

48) TYPE: M   LEVEL: 2   TEXT REFERENCE: 10-10
ANSWER: A

The orbital diagram for lithium is:

```
    1s  2s    2p
A. ⊗   ∅    0 0 0 .
B. ∅   ∅    ∅ 0 0 .
C. ⊗   ⊗    0 0 0 .
D. ⊗   ∅    ∅ 0 0 .
```

49) TYPE: M   LEVEL: 2   TEXT REFERENCE: 10-10
ANSWER: B

Which of the following diagrams represents an atom that is not in its
ground state?

```
    1s   2s      2p
A. ⊗    ⊗     ∅ ∅ 0
B. ⊗    ⊗     ⊗ 0 0
C. ⊗    ⊗     ∅ ∅ ∅
D. ⊗    ⊗     ⊗ ∅ ∅
```

50) TYPE: M   LEVEL: 2   TEXT REFERENCE: 10-10
ANSWER: D

The following electron configuration is read:

$$1s^2 2s^2 2p^4$$

A. "1s two, 2s two, 4p two".
B. "1s squared, 2s squared, 2p squared".
C. "1s squared, 2s squared, 2p to the fourth".
D. "1s two, 2s two, 2p four".

51) TYPE: M   LEVEL: 2   TEXT REFERENCE: 10-10
ANSWER: C

What is the electron configuration for chlorine?

A. $1s^2 2s^2 2p^6 3s^5$
B. $1s^2 2s^2 2p^6 3s^6$
C. $1s^2 2s^2 2p^6 3s^2 3p^5$
D. $1s^2 2s^2 2p^6 3s^2 3p^6$

Chapter 10   ELECTRONS IN ATOMS

52) **TYPE:** M   **LEVEL:** 2   **TEXT REFERENCE:** 10-10
ANSWER: B

What is the electron configuration for the following orbital diagram?

```
1s   2s      2p       3s       3p       4s        3d
⊗    ⊗     ⊗ ⊗ ⊗     ⊗      ⊗ ⊗ ⊗     ⊗     ⊘ ⊘ ◯ ◯ ◯
```

A. $1s^22s^22p^63s^23p^64s^23d$
B. $1s^22s^22p^63s^23p^64s^23d^2$
C. $1s^22s^22p^63s^26p^32s^43d$
D. $1s^22s^22p^63s^26p^34s^22d^3$

53) **TYPE:** M   **LEVEL:** 2   **TEXT REFERENCE:** 10-11
ANSWER: D

What is the orbital diagram for the Na⁺ ion?

```
    1s   2s      2p        3s
A.  ⊗    ⊗    ⊗  ⊗  ⊗     ⊘
B.  ⊗    ⊗    ⊗  ⊗  ⊗     ⊗
C.  ⊗    ⊗    ⊗  ⊗  ⊘     ⊘
D.  ⊗    ⊗    ⊗  ⊗  ⊗     ◯
```


54) **TYPE:** M   **LEVEL:** 2   **TEXT REFERENCE:** 10-11
ANSWER: C

The electron configuration for a chloride ion that contains one
electron more than the neutral chlorine atom is:

A. $1s^22s^22p^63s^23p^5$.
B. $1s^22s^22p^63s^23p^4$.
C. $1s^22s^22p^63s^23p^6$.
D. $1s^22s^22p^63s^33p^5$.

55) **TYPE:** O   **LEVEL:** 4   **TEXT REFERENCE:** LA
ANSWER: incandescent

A continuous band of color containing a large amount of red light is
characteristic of the _____ spectrum.

56) **TYPE:** M   **LEVEL:** 4   **TEXT REFERENCE:** LA
ANSWER: C

If the frequency of the light wave of a photon is known, what may be
calculated?

A. Planck's constant   C. the energy of the photon
B. Bohr's constant   D. the emission spectrum

57) TYPE: M   LEVEL: 4   TEXT REFERENCE: LA
ANSWER: A

White light passed through a prism produces:

A. a continuous spectrum.   C. an emission spectrum.
B. a single color.   D. white light.

58) TYPE: M   LEVEL: 4   TEXT REFERENCE: LA
ANSWER: B

The energy that electrons emit when returning to ground state is:

A. thermal energy.   C. spectral energy.
B. electromagnetic   D. none of the above.
   radiation.

Chapter 11   THE PERIODIC TABLE

1) TYPE: T   LEVEL: 1   TEXT REFERENCE: 11-1
ANSWER: T

_____   The elements in the periodic table are arranged in order of
        increasing atomic number.

2) TYPE: T   LEVEL: 1   TEXT REFERENCE: 11-2
ANSWER: F

_____   Chemical families are grouped in horizontal rows.

3) TYPE: T   LEVEL: 1   TEXT REFERENCE: 11-2
ANSWER: F

_____   The noble gases are the most reactive gases.

4) TYPE: T   LEVEL: 1   TEXT REFERENCE: 11-2
ANSWER: T

_____   Each group in the representative elements is very distinctive.

5) TYPE: T   LEVEL: 2   TEXT REFERENCE: 11-3
ANSWER: T

_____   The 3rd orbital system is being filled in the fourth period
        transition elements.

6) TYPE: T   LEVEL: 1   TEXT REFERENCE: 11-3
ANSWER: F

_____   The s and p orbitals of the noble gases are empty.

7) TYPE: T   LEVEL: 1   TEXT REFERENCE: 11-3
ANSWER: T

_____   The electron configuration of an atom is related to its
        reactivity.

8) TYPE: T   LEVEL: 2   TEXT REFERENCE: 11-3
ANSWER: T

_____   Magnesium is more reactive than krypton.

9) TYPE: T   LEVEL: 1   TEXT REFERENCE: 11-4
ANSWER: F

_____ Metals tend to gain electrons, while nonmetals tend to lose
electrons when becoming isoelectronic with noble gases.

10) TYPE: T   LEVEL: 1   TEXT REFERENCE: 11-4
ANSWER: F

_____ An atom whose outermost s and p orbital system is occupied by
eight electrons tends to be very reactive.

11) TYPE: T   LEVEL: 1   TEXT REFERENCE: 11-4
ANSWER: T

_____ The alkali metals are very reactive.

12) TYPE: T   LEVEL: 1   TEXT REFERENCE: 11-5
ANSWER: T

_____ Both the atomic radii and the ionic radii seem to increase from
top to bottom in a group in the periodic table.

13) TYPE: T   LEVEL: 2   TEXT REFERENCE: 11-5
ANSWER: T

_____ The positive ion of potassium is smaller than the neutral atom
of potassium.

14) TYPE: T   LEVEL: 1   TEXT REFERENCE: 11-6
ANSWER: F

_____ An alkali metal has the highest first ionization energy in its
period.

15) TYPE: O   LEVEL: 1   TEXT REFERENCE: 11-1
ANSWER: numbers

The periodic law states: the properties of the elements recur
periodically when the elements are arranged in increasing order by
their atomic _____.

16) TYPE: O   LEVEL: 1   TEXT REFERENCE: 11-2
ANSWER: families

Elements grouped vertically are known as chemical _____.

17) TYPE: 0   LEVEL: 1   TEXT REFERENCE: 11-2
ANSWER: alkali

Group 1 is known as the _____ metals.

18) TYPE: 0   LEVEL: 1   TEXT REFERENCE: 11-2
ANSWER: transition

Groups 3 to 12 are the _____ elements.

19) TYPE: 0   LEVEL: 1   TEXT REFERENCE: 11-2
ANSWER: lanthanide

The elements with atomic numbers 57 to 71 are the _____
series.

20) TYPE: 0   LEVEL: 1   TEXT REFERENCE: 11-2
ANSWER: 1

Sodium is a member of Group _____.

21) TYPE: 0   LEVEL: 1   TEXT REFERENCE: 11-3
ANSWER: eight

The s and p orbitals can be occupied by a maximum of _____
electrons.

22) TYPE: 0   LEVEL: 2   TEXT REFERENCE: 11-3
ANSWER: $1s^2 2s^2 2p^6 3s^2$

The electron configuration for magnesium, atomic number 12, is
_____.

23) TYPE: 0   LEVEL: 1   TEXT REFERENCE: 11-3
ANSWER: valence

The electrons in the outermost s and p orbitals are referred to as
_____ electrons.

24) TYPE: 0   LEVEL: 1   TEXT REFERENCE: 11-4
ANSWER: isoelectronic

Atoms and ions of different elements with the same electron
configuration are said to be _____.

25)   TYPE: 0   LEVEL: 2   TEXT REFERENCE: 11-4
ANSWER: $1s^2 2s^2 2p^6$

The electron configuration for the fluoride ion, F⁻, (atomic no. 9)
is _____.

26)   TYPE: 0   LEVEL: 1   TEXT REFERENCE: 11-5
ANSWER: decrease

Atomic radii _____ from left to right across the
periodic table.

27)   TYPE: 0   LEVEL: 1   TEXT REFERENCE: 11-5
ANSWER: increase

Atomic radii _____ from top to bottom in a group or
family.

28)   TYPE: 0   LEVEL: 1   TEXT REFERENCE: 11-5
ANSWER: increase

Ionic radii _____ from top to bottom in a group or
family.

29)   TYPE: 0   LEVEL: 1   TEXT REFERENCE: 11-5
ANSWER: larger

A negative ion is _____ than the neutral atom of an
element.

30)   TYPE: 0   LEVEL: 1   TEXT REFERENCE: 11-6
ANSWER: ionization

The energy needed to remove an electron from a neutral gaseous atom
is known as the _____ energy.

31)   TYPE: 0   LEVEL: 2   TEXT REFERENCE: 11-6
ANSWER: krypton

The noble gas _____ has a higher ionization energy
than any other element in the same period.

32)   TYPE: 0   LEVEL: 2   TEXT REFERENCE: 11-6
ANSWER: smaller

The ionization energy of an atom with a large molar mass will be
_____ than the ionization energy of an atom in the same
family with a relatively small molar mass.

33) TYPE: M   LEVEL: 2   TEXT REFERENCE: 11-2
ANSWER: B

Which of the following is not a metal?

A. Li   C. Na
B. Kr   D. K

34) TYPE: M   LEVEL: 1   TEXT REFERENCE: 11-2
ANSWER: D

Group 17 includes the:

A. alkali earth metals.   C. rare earth metals.
B. noble gases.   D. halogens.

35) TYPE: M   LEVEL: 1   TEXT REFERENCE: 11-2
ANSWER: B

The term "transition element" is used to describe elements in the:

A. left side of the periodic table.
B. middle of the periodic table.
C. right side of the periodic table.
D. groups 1,2,13,14,15,16,17, and 18.

36) TYPE: M   LEVEL: 1   TEXT REFERENCE: 11-2
ANSWER: B

Elements 93 to 109 are called the:

A. representative elements.   C. transition elements.
B. transuranium elements.   D. noble gases.

37) TYPE: M   LEVEL: 2   TEXT REFERENCE: 11-3
ANSWER: A

Each alkali metal has how many electrons in the outermost orbital?

A. one   C. two
B. five   D. seven

38) TYPE: M   LEVEL: 2   TEXT REFERENCE: 11-3
ANSWER: C

Which of the following elements does not have eight electrons in its outermost s and p orbital system?

A. Kr   C. He
B. Ar   D. Xe

39) TYPE: M   LEVEL: 2   TEXT REFERENCE: 11-3
ANSWER: A

What is the electron configuration for sodium, atomic number 11?

A. Na $1s^2 2s^2 2p^6 3s^1$
B. Na $1s^2 2s^2 2p^6$
C. Na $1s^2 2s^2 2p^5 3s^2$
D. Na $1s^2 2s^2 2p^7$

40) TYPE: M   LEVEL: 2   TEXT REFERENCE: 11-4
ANSWER: A

Nonmetals generally form what type of ions?

A. negative
B. positive
C. neutral
D. depends on the individual nonmetal

41) TYPE: M   LEVEL: 2   TEXT REFERENCE: 11-4
ANSWER: C

What is the most likely charge for an ion of magnesium?

A. 2-   C. 2+
B. 1+   D. 0

42) TYPE: M   LEVEL: 2   TEXT REFERENCE: 11-4
ANSWER: A

What is the electron configuration for beryllium, atomic number 4?

A. $1s^2 2s^2$ C. $1s^1 2s^1$
B. $1s^2 2p^2$ D. $1s^2 2p^1$

43) TYPE: M   LEVEL: 2   TEXT REFERENCE: 11-4
ANSWER: C

The fluorine ion, F^-, (atomic no. 9) is isoelectronic with:

A. fluorine-9   C. neon-10
B. argon-18   D. sodium-11

44)   TYPE: M   LEVEL: 1   TEXT REFERENCE: 11-5
ANSWER: D

The atomic radius is one-half the distance between:

A. the outermost electrons of bonded atoms.
B. the innermost electrons of bonded atoms.
C. atoms in a gas.
D. the nuclei of bonded atoms.

45)   TYPE: M   LEVEL: 2   TEXT REFERENCE: 11-5
ANSWER: B

An element at the top of a family will have a(n):

A. larger atomic radius than an element below it.
B. smaller atomic radius than an element below it.
C. larger ionic radius than an element below it.
D. atomic radius equal to the elements in its family.

46)   TYPE: M   LEVEL: 1   TEXT REFERENCE: 11-5
ANSWER: C

The shielding effect causes a weakening of the forces between the:

A. inner and outer electrons.
B. nucleus and inner electrons.
C. nucleus and outer electrons.
D. protons and inner electrons.

47)   TYPE: M   LEVEL: 2   TEXT REFERENCE: 11-5
ANSWER: D

Which of the following elements has the smallest atomic radius?

A. Al   C. P
B. S   D. Cl

48)   TYPE: M   LEVEL: 2   TEXT REFERENCE: 11-5
ANSWER: D

Which noble gas will have an atomic radius larger than the atomic
radius of argon?

A. Ne   C. Kr
B. Xe   D. Both Kr and Xe

49) TYPE: M   LEVEL: 2   TEXT REFERENCE: 11-5
ANSWER: B

If the outermost electron of a neutral potassium atom is removed, the
resulting ion will be:

A. larger than the neutral atom.
B. smaller than the neutral atom.
C. the same size as the neutral atom.
D. one-half the size of the original atom.

50) TYPE: M   LEVEL: 2   TEXT REFERENCE: 11-6
ANSWER: B

Which equation correctly represents the ionization process?

A. element + ionization energy $\rightarrow$ ion + 1e
B. element(g) + ionization energy $\rightarrow$ ion$^+$(g) + 1e$^-$
C. element(g) + ionization energy $\rightarrow$ ion$^-$(g) + 1e$^+$
D. element(g) + ionization energy $\rightarrow$ ion$^+$ + 1e$^-$

51) TYPE: M   LEVEL: 2   TEXT REFERENCE: 11-6
ANSWER: B

An element with a low ionization energy forms:

A. negative ions.   C. no ions.
B. positive ions.   D. diatomic ions.

52) TYPE: M   LEVEL: 2   TEXT REFERENCE: 11-6
ANSWER: D

Which atom will have a higher first ionization energy than argon,
whose electron configuration is $1s^2 2s^2 2p^6 3s^2 3p^6$?

A. Na $1s^2 2s^2 2p^6 3s^1$
B. Be $1s^2 2s^2$
C. Cl $1s^2 2s^2 2p^6 3s^2 3p^5$
D. none of the above

53) TYPE: M   LEVEL: 2   TEXT REFERENCE: 11-6
ANSWER: A

If a metal is isoelectronic with a noble gas, it will be:

A. difficult to remove an electron.
B. easy to remove an electron.
C. difficult to add an electron.
D. cannot tell.

54) TYPE: M   LEVEL: 4   TEXT REFERENCE: LA
ANSWER: C

Elements with identical numbers of electrons in their outermost
sublevels are in the same:

A. family.   C. group
B. group and family.   D. cannot tell.

55) TYPE: M   LEVEL: 4   TEXT REFERENCE: LA
ANSWER: A

In each period, the largest atomic radius is associated with the:

A. group 1 member.   C. group 8 member.
B. group 18 member.   D. none of the above.

56) TYPE: M   LEVEL: 4   TEXT REFERENCE: LA
ANSWER: C

What factor may account for the trend that atomic radii become
smaller across a period?

A. decreased nuclear charge
B. electrons orbit in a larger area
C. increased nuclear charge
D. decrease in ionization energies

Chapter 12   CHEMICAL BONDING

1) TYPE: T   LEVEL: 1   TEXT REFERENCE: 12-1
ANSWER: T

____   Bond energy is a measure of bond strength.

2) TYPE: T   LEVEL: 1   TEXT REFERENCE: 12-3
ANSWER: F

____   Atoms in a covalent bond always share electrons equally.

3) TYPE: T   LEVEL: 2   TEXT REFERENCE: 12-3
ANSWER: T

____   A polar covalent bond is a covalent bond with a dipole.

4) TYPE: T   LEVEL: 1   TEXT REFERENCE: 12-4
ANSWER: F

____   Ionic bonding occurs between two metallic elements.

5) TYPE: T   LEVEL: 1   TEXT REFERENCE: 12-5
ANSWER: F

____   The chemical symbol in an electron dot structure is used to
       represent the nucleus and all the electrons of an atom,
       including the valence electrons.

6) TYPE: T   LEVEL: 1   TEXT REFERENCE: 12-5
ANSWER: F

____   Atoms of two different elements in the same period of the
       periodic table have the same electron dot structure.

7) TYPE: T   LEVEL: 1   TEXT REFERENCE: 12-7
ANSWER: T

____   The octet rule cannot adequately diagram molecules that contain
       an odd number of valence electrons.

8) TYPE: T   LEVEL: 1   TEXT REFERENCE: 12-8
ANSWER: F

____   Energy is released when a bond is broken.

9) TYPE: T   LEVEL: 3   TEXT REFERENCE: 12-9
ANSWER: T

_____   In order to change position in an atom, electrons must absorb
        or emit a specific amount of energy.

10) TYPE: T   LEVEL: 3   TEXT REFERENCE: 12-10
ANSWER: F

_____   Resonance structures are used to show the different bond
        energies within a molecule.

11) TYPE: T   LEVEL: 1   TEXT REFERENCE: 12-12
ANSWER: F

_____   Polar bonds always produce polar molecules.

12) TYPE: T   LEVEL: 1   TEXT REFERENCE: 12-13
ANSWER: F

_____   A hydrogen bond occurs when the hydrogen atom of a polar
        molecule is attracted to the positive end of another polar
        molecule.

13) TYPE: O   LEVEL: 1   TEXT REFERENCE: 12-2
ANSWER: nuclei

A chemical bond can form between two atoms when electrons are
attracted simultaneously to both atomic _____.

14) TYPE: O   LEVEL: 1   TEXT REFERENCE: 12-2
ANSWER: covalent

A(n) _____ bond is the result of a sharing of
electrons between two atoms.

15) TYPE: O   LEVEL: 1   TEXT REFERENCE: 12-2
ANSWER: decrease

The sharing of electrons results in a(n) _____ in the
energy of the system.

16) TYPE: O   LEVEL: 2   TEXT REFERENCE: 12-3
ANSWER: covalent

The bond between oxygen atoms in O_2 is classified as a(n)
_____ bond.

17) TYPE: O   LEVEL: 1   TEXT REFERENCE: 12-3
ANSWER: electronegativity

The attraction an atom has for the shared pair of electrons in a covalent bond is called the atom's _____.

18) TYPE: O   LEVEL: 2   TEXT REFERENCE: 12-3
ANSWER: ionic

The bond between Li and O in Li_2O is classified as _____.

19) TYPE: O   LEVEL: 1   TEXT REFERENCE: 12-4
ANSWER: lattice

A regular, three-dimensional arrangement of positive and negative ions is called a crystal _____.

20) TYPE: O   LEVEL: 1   TEXT REFERENCE: 12-5
ANSWER: valence

The electrons in the outermost s and p orbitals are known as the _____ electrons.

21) TYPE: O   LEVEL: 1   TEXT REFERENCE: 12-5
ANSWER: Lewis

Electron dot structures are often called _____ structures.

22) TYPE: O   LEVEL: 1   TEXT REFERENCE: 12-6
ANSWER: octet

The assumption for the _____ rule is that nonmetals will bond together in such a way as to have eight electrons in their outermost energy level.

23) TYPE: O   LEVEL: 1   TEXT REFERENCE: 12-6
ANSWER: four

A double bond is a covalent bond in which _____ electrons are being shared by two bonding atoms.

24) TYPE: O   LEVEL: 1   TEXT REFERENCE: 12-6
ANSWER: three

A triple bond is a covalent bond in which two atoms share _____ pairs of electrons.

25) **TYPE:** 0   **LEVEL:** 1   **TEXT REFERENCE:** 12-8
ANSWER: increases

The potential energy of a system _____ when the chemical bonds are broken.

26) **TYPE:** 0   **LEVEL:** 1   **TEXT REFERENCE:** 12-8
ANSWER: bond

The energy needed to separate two bonded atoms is the _____ energy.

27) **TYPE:** 0   **LEVEL:** 1   **TEXT REFERENCE:** 12-8
ANSWER: harder

In a triple bond, the second bond is usually _____ to break than the third bond.

28) **TYPE:** 0   **LEVEL:** 3   **TEXT REFERENCE:** 12-10
ANSWER: resonance

The various structures used to represent a molecule that cannot be represented by one diagram are known as _____ structures.

29) **TYPE:** 0   **LEVEL:** 2   **TEXT REFERENCE:** 12-11
ANSWER: linear

A molecule such as MgH_2 has a(n) _____ shape.

30) **TYPE:** 0   **LEVEL:** 1   **TEXT REFERENCE:** 12-11
ANSWER: trigonal

BF_3 has a(n) _____ planar shape.

31) **TYPE:** 0   **LEVEL:** 1   **TEXT REFERENCE:** 12-11
ANSWER: angular

An H_2O molecule has a spatial arrangement known as

_____.

32) **TYPE:** 0   **LEVEL:** 1   **TEXT REFERENCE:** 12-12
ANSWER: intermolecular

An attraction that takes place between molecules is called

_____.

33) **TYPE:** O   **LEVEL:** 1   **TEXT REFERENCE:** 12-12
ANSWER: polar

Dipole-dipole forces occur between _____ molecules.

34) **TYPE:** O   **LEVEL:** 2   **TEXT REFERENCE:** 12-14
ANSWER: London

The forces that result in weak attractions between Ne atoms are
called _____ forces.

35) **TYPE:** M   **LEVEL:** 1   **TEXT REFERENCE:** 12-2
ANSWER: B

In order for a chemical bond to form between two atoms the attractive
forces must be greater than the:

A. potential energy.   C. covalent bond.
B. repulsive forces.   D. electrical force.

36) **TYPE:** M   **LEVEL:** 2   **TEXT REFERENCE:** 12-3
ANSWER: A

In a covalent bond between hydrogen and fluorine, the fluorine has:

A. a greater electronegativity than hydrogen.
B. a smaller electronegativity than hydrogen.
C. the same electronegativity as hydrogen.
D. a charge of 1+.

37) **TYPE:** M   **LEVEL:** 1   **TEXT REFERENCE:** 12-3
ANSWER: B

A pair of bonding electrons is considered to be shared equally if the
difference in the electronegativity of the atoms involved is:

A. 0.2 or more.   C. 1.7 or more.
B. 0.2 or less.   D. 1.7 or less.

38) **TYPE:** M   **LEVEL:** 2   **TEXT REFERENCE:** 12-3
ANSWER: D

The S-O bond in SO_2 is classified as a(n):

A. covalent bond.   C. dipole bond.
B. ionic bond.   D. polar covalent bond.

39) TYPE: M   LEVEL: 1   TEXT REFERENCE: 12-3
ANSWER: A

The bond in NaCl is classified as:

A. ionic.   C. covalent.
B. polar covalent.   D. nonpolar.

40) TYPE: M   LEVEL: 1   TEXT REFERENCE: 12-3
ANSWER: D

The difference between the electronegativities of two atoms in an
ionic bond is:

A. 0.2 or less.   C. 1.7 or less.
B. 0.2 or greater.   D. 1.7 or greater.

41) TYPE: M   LEVEL: 2   TEXT REFERENCE: 12-5
ANSWER: C

The electron dot structure for sodium would have the same number of
dots as the electron dot structure for:

A. flourine.   C. potassium.
B. oxygen.   D. argon.

42) TYPE: M   LEVEL: 1   TEXT REFERENCE: 12-6
ANSWER: B

A double bond is a covalent bond in which:

A. two electrons are shared by two atoms.
B. four electrons are shared by two atoms.
C. four electrons are shared by four atoms.
D. two electrons are shared by four atoms.

43) TYPE: M   LEVEL: 2   TEXT REFERENCE: 12-6
ANSWER: D

How may the bond structure for H_2 be represented?

A. 2H   C. H-H
B. H:H   D. either B or C

44) TYPE: M   LEVEL: 1   TEXT REFERENCE: 12-8
ANSWER: B

When bonds form in a system, the potential energy of the system:

A. increases.   C. stays the same.
B. decreases.   D. cannot tell.

45) TYPE: M   LEVEL: 2   TEXT REFERENCE: 12-8
ANSWER: B

The first bond of a double bond is:

A. weaker than the second bond.
B. stronger than the second bond.
C. the same as the second bond.
D. either stronger or weaker, depending on the molecule.

46) TYPE: M   LEVEL: 2   TEXT REFERENCE: 12-8
ANSWER: C

Which of the following molecules is least reactive?

A. C_2H_2
B. C_2H_4
C. C_2H_6
D. all are equally reactive

47) TYPE: M   LEVEL: 3   TEXT REFERENCE: 12-9
ANSWER: B

Energy for the transition of molecular vibrations would be detected
in the:

A. ultraviolet regions of the electromagnetic spectrum.
B. infrared region of the electromagnetic spectrum.
C. microwave regions of the electromagnetic spectrum.
D. infrared region of the visible spectrum.

48) TYPE: M   LEVEL: 3   TEXT REFERENCE: 12-10
ANSWER: C

If a molecule is represented by three resonance structures, it:

A. may exist in three different states.
B. has three different ions.
C. has a structure that cannot be represented by one model.
D. probably is capable of forming triple bonds.

49) TYPE: M   LEVEL: 2   TEXT REFERENCE: 12-11
ANSWER: C

The molecule PH_3 may be predicted to have what shape?

A. trigonal planar
B. tetrahedral
C. trigonal pyramidal
D. trigonal bipyramidal

50) TYPE: M   LEVEL: 1   TEXT REFERENCE: 12-11
ANSWER: C

VSEPR stands for:

A. valence shape electron parts repulsion test.
B. valence shape electron pair repulsion test.
C. valence shell electron pair repulsion theory.
D. valence shell electron parts resonance theory.

51) TYPE: M   LEVEL: 2   TEXT REFERENCE: 12-12
ANSWER: D

The nonpolar molecule BeH_2 contains:

A. one polar bond.   C. two nonpolar bonds.
B. one nonpolar bond.   D. two polar bonds.

52) TYPE: M   LEVEL: 1   TEXT REFERENCE: 12-12
ANSWER: C

Forces occuring within the same molecule are said to be:

A. covalent.   C. intramolecular.
B. intermolecular.   D. dipole-dipole forces.

53) TYPE: M   LEVEL: 1   TEXT REFERENCE: 12-14
ANSWER: D

At any given instant, an uneven distribution of electrons in an atom
would result in a(n):

A. dipole-dipole force.   C. permanent dipole.
B. London force.   D. momentary dipole.

54) TYPE: M   LEVEL: 2   TEXT REFERENCE: 12-14
ANSWER: A

Which of the following is subject to the weakest van der Waals
forces?

A. He   C. H_2O
B. NH_3 D. BF_3

55) TYPE: M   LEVEL: 2   TEXT REFERENCE: 12-14
ANSWER: B

Molecules such as CH_4, whose dipoles cancel:

A. are polar.
B. are nonpolar.
C. interact through ionic attractions.
D. interact through hydrogen bonds.

56) TYPE: M   LEVEL: 4   TEXT REFERENCE: LA
ANSWER: A

Predict the melting time of potassium nitrate:

A. relatively long.
B. relatively short.
C. cannot tell.
D. similar to that of benzoic acid.

57) TYPE: M   LEVEL: 4   TEXT REFERENCE: LA
ANSWER: D

The melting time of sucrose is most similar to the melting time of:

A. benzoic acid.   C. magnesium chloride.
B. sodium nitrate.   D. none of the above.

58) TYPE: M   LEVEL: 4   TEXT REFERENCE: LA
ANSWER: C

As a general rule, solids are more soluble in:

A. cold water than in hot water.
B. neither hot nor cold water.
C. hot water than in cold water.
D. cannot tell.

59) TYPE: O   LEVEL: 4   TEXT REFERENCE: LB
ANSWER: C

The shape of a water molecule is called:

A. linear.   C. angular.
B. trigonal.   D. trigonal pyramidal.

60) TYPE: M   LEVEL: 4   TEXT REFERENCE: LB
ANSWER: B

The shape of a carbon dioxide molecule is:

A. trigonal.   C. tetrahedral.
B. linear.   D. none of the above.

61) TYPE: M   LEVEL: 4   TEXT REFERENCE: LB
ANSWER: A

How many different structural isomers can be drawn for the formula
C_4H_{10}?

A. 2   C. 1
B. 4   D. any number

Chapter 13 ELEMENTS: A CLOSER LOOK

1) TYPE: T   LEVEL: 1   TEXT REFERENCE: 13-1
ANSWER: F

_____ The distances between energy levels in metallic solids is very
       large.

2) TYPE: T   LEVEL: 1   TEXT REFERENCE: 13-1
ANSWER: T

_____ The atoms in a metal are arranged in a crystal structure with
       electrons from the outer most energy levels spread throughout
       the crystal.

3) TYPE: T   LEVEL: 1   TEXT REFERENCE: 13-2
ANSWER: T

_____ Pure alkali metals are soft enough to be cut with a knife.

4) TYPE: T   LEVEL: 1   TEXT REFERENCE: 13-3
ANSWER: F

_____ Alkaline-earth metals are more reactive than alkali metals.

5) TYPE: T   LEVEL: 1   TEXT REFERENCE: 13-5
ANSWER: F

_____ The fourth-row transition elements all contain two electrons in
       the 4s orbital.

6) TYPE: T   LEVEL: 1   TEXT REFERENCE: 13-6
ANSWER: T

_____ Silver conducts electricity better than copper.

7) TYPE: T   LEVEL: 1   TEXT REFERENCE: 13-6
ANSWER: T

_____ The primary industrial use for silver is in photographic
       film.

8) TYPE: T   LEVEL: 1   TEXT REFERENCE: 13-7
ANSWER: T

_____ Stainless steel is an alloy of iron.

9) TYPE: T   LEVEL: 1   TEXT REFERENCE: 13-9
ANSWER: T

____ Metalloids are poor conductors of electricity.

10) TYPE: T   LEVEL: 1   TEXT REFERENCE: 13-10
ANSWER: T

____ Silicones can be used to protect metals from corrosion.

11) TYPE: T   LEVEL: 2   TEXT REFERENCE: 13-11
ANSWER: T

____ One of the best ways to preserve food is to pack it in nitrogen
      gas.

12) TYPE: T   LEVEL: 1   TEXT REFERENCE: 13-12
ANSWER: F

____ Sulfates are synthetic compounds.

13) TYPE: T   LEVEL: 2   TEXT REFERENCE: 13-13
ANSWER: T

____ Chlorine is a very common halogen that exists in nature as a
      yellow-green gas.

14) TYPE: T   LEVEL: 1   TEXT REFERENCE: 13-14
ANSWER: T

____ The major use of noble gases is in welding.

15) TYPE: O   LEVEL: 2   TEXT REFERENCE: 13-1
ANSWER: ductility

A metal that is easily formed into wire has good _____.

16) TYPE: O   LEVEL: 1   TEXT REFERENCE: 13-2
ANSWER: reactivity

The alkali metals are not found in nature in the elemental state due
to their high chemical _____.

17) TYPE: O   LEVEL: 2   TEXT REFERENCE: 13-3
ANSWER: alloy

A mixture of magnesium and aluminum is called a(n) _____.

18) TYPE: O   LEVEL: 1   TEXT REFERENCE: 13-4
ANSWER: alum

A(n) _____ compound is an aluminum sulfate.

19) TYPE: O   LEVEL: 1   TEXT REFERENCE: 13-5
ANSWER: lose

Metals are defined chemically as elements that tend to _____
electrons in the presence of other elements.

20) TYPE: O   LEVEL: 1   TEXT REFERENCE: 13-5
ANSWER: iron

The most abundant fourth-row transition element is _____.

21) TYPE: O   LEVEL: 1   TEXT REFERENCE: 13-5
ANSWER: noble

Transition elements such as gold, silver, and platinum are referred
to as "_____ metals" because of their low reactivity.

22) TYPE: O   LEVEL: 1   TEXT REFERENCE: 13-9
ANSWER: metalloids

The properties of _____ are intermediate between metals and
nonmetals.

23) TYPE: O   LEVEL: 1   TEXT REFERENCE: 13-10
ANSWER: allotropes

Elements that can have more than one molecular structure in the same
physical state are called _____.

24) TYPE: O   LEVEL: 1   TEXT REFERENCE: 13-10
ANSWER: silicon

The second most abundant element in Earth's crust is
_____.

25) TYPE: O   LEVEL: 1   TEXT REFERENCE: 13-11
ANSWER: three

There are _____ common allotropes of phosphorus.

26) TYPE: O   LEVEL: 1   TEXT REFERENCE: 13-13
ANSWER: halogen

The name _____ means "salt-former."

27) TYPE: O   LEVEL: 1   TEXT REFERENCE: 13-13
ANSWER: fluorine

The most active element is _____.

28) TYPE: O   LEVEL: 2   TEXT REFERENCE: 13-13
ANSWER: increases

The reactivity of halogens decreases as the atomic mass
_____.

29) TYPE: O   LEVEL: 1   TEXT REFERENCE: 13-14
ANSWER: argon

The first noble gas to be discovered was named _____,
meaning "no work."

30) TYPE: M   LEVEL: 1   TEXT REFERENCE: 13-1
ANSWER: B

The characteristic of a metal that allows it to be shaped without
breaking is called its:

A. ductility.   C. alloyability.
B. malleability.   D. localization.

31) TYPE: M   LEVEL: 2   TEXT REFERENCE: 13-2
ANSWER: A

Which of the following substances would not be used to store a block
of pure cesium?

A. water   C. "dry" liquid hydrogen
B. kerosene   D. nonaqueous liquid hydrogen

32) TYPE: M   LEVEL: 2   TEXT REFERENCE: 13-2
ANSWER: B

Which of the following is a characteristic of all alkali metals?

A. They are poor conductors of heat.
B. They form ionic compounds.
C. Their outer energy levels all contain two electrons.
D. They have low malleability.

33)   TYPE: M   LEVEL: 1   TEXT REFERENCE: 13-2
ANSWER: C

Hydroxide is produced when an alkali metal reacts with:

A. sodium.   C. water.
B. air.   D. hydrogen.

34) TYPE: M   LEVEL: 1   TEXT REFERENCE: 13-3
ANSWER: D

The properties of an alloy are the same as:

A. the properties of the most reactive element it contains.
B. the properties of the least reactive element it contains.
C. the properties of the nonreactive element it contains.
D. none of the properties of the elements it contains.

35) TYPE: M   LEVEL: 2   TEXT REFERENCE: 13-4
ANSWER: B

An aluminum-magnesium alloy would most likely be used in:

A. water purification   C. baking powder.
B. a bicycle.   D. insulation.

36) TYPE: M   LEVEL: 1   TEXT REFERENCE: 13-5
ANSWER: B

The melting points of the fourth-row transition elements:

A. increase toward the end of the group.
B. decrease toward the end of the group.
C. are the same for every member.
D. are all relatively low.

37) TYPE: M   LEVEL: 1   TEXT REFERENCE: 13-5
ANSWER: C

The ionization energies for the fourth-row transition elements:

A. decrease slightly across the row.
B. decrease sharply across the row.
C. increase slightly across the row.
D. increase sharply across the row.

38) **TYPE:** M   **LEVEL:** 1   **TEXT REFERENCE:** 13-6
ANSWER: D

Copper is easily separated from copper compounds by a process called:

A. electrolysis   C. tarnishing.
B. electroplating.   D. roasting.

39) **TYPE:** M   **LEVEL:** 2   **TEXT REFERENCE:** 13-6
ANSWER: B

Which of the following elements would be most desireable to use as
electrical wire?

A. chromium   C. steel
B. copper   D. iron

40) **TYPE:** M   **LEVEL:** 1   **TEXT REFERENCE:** 13-6
ANSWER: B

Silver tarnishes when it comes in contact with:

A. air.
B. hydrogen sulfide.
C. water.
D. oxygen and sulfur.

41) **TYPE:** M   **LEVEL:** 2   **TEXT REFERENCE:** 13-6
ANSWER: D

What is the oxidation number of the transition element in MnO_2?

A. 1+   C. 6+
B. 2+   D. 4+

42) **TYPE:** M   **LEVEL:** 2   **TEXT REFERENCE:** 13-7
ANSWER: D

What alloy of iron would make the best water faucet?

A. pig iron   C. tempered steel
B. cast iron   D. stainless steel

43) TYPE: M   LEVEL: 3   TEXT REFERENCE: 13-8
ANSWER: C

The color of gems is due to bonding and the:

A. reflection of visible light.
B. reflection of unpaired electrons.
C. absorption of visible light.
D. absorption of colored light.

44) TYPE: M   LEVEL: 2   TEXT REFERENCE: 13-9
ANSWER: D

Which of the following elements is a semiconductor?

A. Fe   C. Ag
B. O   D. As

45) TYPE: M   LEVEL: 2   TEXT REFERENCE: 13-10
ANSWER: B

Which of the following metalloids would be most effective as a weed
killer?

A. boron   C. silicon
B. arsenic   D. germanium

46) TYPE: M   LEVEL: 1   TEXT REFERENCE: 13-11
ANSWER: D

Elements that have a strong tendency to accept electrons in the
presence of other elements are:

A. alkali metals.   C. metalloids.
B. alkaline-earth metals.   D. nonmetals.

47) TYPE: M   LEVEL: 1   TEXT REFERENCE: 13-12
ANSWER: C

Oxygen is vital to life due to the roles it has in:

A. altering the function of enzymes.
B. joining amino acids.
C. cellular respiration.
D. the production of ozone.

48)   TYPE: M   LEVEL: 1   TEXT REFERENCE: 13-13
ANSWER: D

Which of the following is not a characteristic of the halogens?

A. reactive   C. high electronegativities
B. nonmetallic   D. colorless

49)   TYPE: M   LEVEL: 1   TEXT REFERENCE: 13-13
ANSWER: A

Which halogen can replace chlorine?

A. fluorine   C. iodine
B. bromine   D. astatine

50)   TYPE: M   LEVEL: 4   TEXT REFERENCE: LA
ANSWER: A

If zinc, a gray, shiny metal, is sandpapered, it becomes:

A. more shiny.   C. dull.
B. white.   D. orange.

51)   TYPE: M   LEVEL: 4   TEXT REFERENCE: LA
ANSWER: C

Which of the following metals is the most malleable?

A. magnesium   C. copper
B. zinc   D. iron

52)   TYPE: M   LEVEL: 4   TEXT REFERENCE: LA
ANSWER: A

Which of the following metals reacts rapidly in water?

A. magnesium   C. copper
B. zinc   D. iron

53)   TYPE: O   LEVEL: 4   TEXT REFERENCE: LB
ANSWER: B

The commonly accepted value for x in the formula $MnCl_x$ is the
number:

A. 1   C. 3
B. 2   D. 4

54) TYPE: M   LEVEL: 4   TEXT REFERENCE: LB
ANSWER: D

Which of the following is a reason that the experimental value
obtained for x in the fomula $MnCl_x$ is not a whole number?

A. loss of some Mn   C. too much HCl
B. impure Mn   D. both A and B

55) TYPE: M   LEVEL: 4   TEXT REFERENCE: LC
ANSWER: D

Which of the following will increase the silver deposition on a
photographic print?

A. addition of developer   C. more light
B. brighter light   D. all of the above

56) TYPE: M   LEVEL: 4   TEXT REFERENCE: LC
ANSWER: A

A solution called a "stop bath" that will stop the development
process is a(n):

A. acid.   C. base.
B. alkaline.   D. silver compound.

1) TYPE: T   LEVEL: 1   TEXT REFERENCE: 14-1
ANSWER: T

____   The electrons in silicon are localized.

2) TYPE: T   LEVEL: 1   TEXT REFERENCE: 14-1
ANSWER: F

____   A pure crystal of silicon is an excellent conductor of
         elecricity.

3) TYPE: T   LEVEL: 1   TEXT REFERENCE: 14-1
ANSWER: T

____   Silicon doped with arsenic forms an n-type semiconductor.

4) TYPE: T   LEVEL: 1   TEXT REFERENCE: 14-1
ANSWER: F

____   Pure silicon crystals bind together in a three-dimensional
         network with many mobile electrons within the solid.

5) TYPE: T   LEVEL: 3   TEXT REFERENCE: 14-2
ANSWER: F

____   A scanning tunneling microscope uses visible light energy to
         view atoms.

6) TYPE: T   LEVEL: 1   TEXT REFERENCE: 14-3
ANSWER: F

____   One advantage of photovoltaic cells is that pure silicon is
         very inexpensive to manufacture.

7) TYPE: T   LEVEL: 1   TEXT REFERENCE: 14-4
ANSWER: F

____   A ceramic is composed of small crystals of the orthosilicate
         ion in a matrix of glassy cement.

8) TYPE: T   LEVEL: 2   TEXT REFERENCE: 14-4
ANSWER: T

____   Porcelain, bricks, and earthenware are all ceramic materials.

9) TYPE: T   LEVEL: 1   TEXT REFERENCE: 14-5
ANSWER: T

____   The mineral quartz and pure silica glass have the same chemical
composition but different structures.

10) TYPE: T   LEVEL: 1   TEXT REFERENCE: 14-5
ANSWER: T

____   Optical fibers can transmit light around corners.

11) TYPE: T   LEVEL: 1   TEXT REFERENCE: 14-5
ANSWER: T

____   Lead oxide added to an alkaline glass will improve the clarity
of the glass.

12) TYPE: T   LEVEL: 1   TEXT REFERENCE: 14-6
ANSWER: T

____   The methods of conducting a literature search are fairly
constant.

13) TYPE: T   LEVEL: 1   TEXT REFERENCE: 14-7
ANSWER: F

____   An encyclopedia is a more specific reference than a magazine.

14) TYPE: O   LEVEL: 1   TEXT REFERENCE: 14-1
ANSWER: doped

Crystals that contain deliberately added impurities are called
_____ crystals.

15) TYPE: O   LEVEL: 2   TEXT REFERENCE: 14-1
ANSWER: p

Silicon with gallium added is called a(n) _____- type
semiconductor.

16) TYPE: O   LEVEL: 1   TEXT REFERENCE: 14-1
ANSWER: n

Semiconductors that have been doped with impurities to produce mobile
electrons are called _____- type semiconductors.

17)   TYPE: O   LEVEL: 1   TEXT REFERENCE: 14-1
ANSWER: integrated

The proper arrangement of components on a single tiny piece of
semiconductor material forms a(n) _____ circuit.

18)   TYPE: O   LEVEL: 1   TEXT REFERENCE: 14-3
ANSWER: photovoltaic

A solar cell, known as a(n) _____ cell, changes
radiation into electricity.

19)   TYPE: O   LEVEL: 2   TEXT REFERENCE: 14-3
ANSWER: 32

A solar cell with a 32% efficiency rating converts _____%
of the energy it receives from the sun to electrical energy.

20)   TYPE: O   LEVEL: 1   TEXT REFERENCE: 14-5
ANSWER: optical

Very fine fibers of glass that transmit light are called
_____ fibers.

21)   TYPE: M   LEVEL: 2   TEXT REFERENCE: 14-1
ANSWER: A

Silicon that is doped with an impurity to produce mobile electrons is
called a(n):

A. n-type semiconductor.   C. "electronic brain."
B. p-type semiconductor.   D. integrated circuit.

22)   TYPE: M   LEVEL: 1   TEXT REFERENCE: 14-1
ANSWER: C

Electrons will have the tendency to flow across a junction toward the:

A. positive electrons in the n-type semiconductor.
B. positive electrons in the p-type semiconductor.
C. positive holes in the p-type semiconductor.
D. negative holes in the n-type semiconductor.

23) TYPE: M   LEVEL: 2   TEXT REFERENCE: 14-1
ANSWER: C

Which of the following is an example of a limitation of
microelectronics?

A. Computers have become smaller.
B. Electron tubes cost more than integrated circuits.
C. Impurities in the semiconductors diffuse.
D. Integrated circuits have cool operating temperatures.

24) TYPE: M   LEVEL: 2   TEXT REFERENCE: 14-1
ANSWER: D

Silicon doped with any impurity will:

A. form an n-type semiconductor.
B. form a p-type semiconductor.
C. not conduct electricity.
D. cannot tell.

25) TYPE: M   LEVEL: 2   TEXT REFERENCE: 14-1
ANSWER: A

Pure silicon crystals are composed of:

A. covalently bonded silicon in a tetrahedral structure.
B. ionic bonds between silicon and a metalloid.
C. covalent bonds between silicon and a metalloid.
D. none of the above.

26) TYPE: M   LEVEL: 3   TEXT REFERENCE: 14-2
ANSWER: D

The scanning tunneling microscope does not:

A. use computer graphics.
B. allow chemists to "see" reactions.
C. show the surface detail of semiconductors.
D. use visible light.

27) TYPE: M   LEVEL: 1   TEXT REFERENCE: 14-3
ANSWER: A

When sunlight strikes a solar cell, electrons flow:

A. from the surface layer to the body of the cell.
B. from the body of the cell to the surface layer.
C. to the p-type semiconductor.
D. to the n-type semiconductor.

28) TYPE: M   LEVEL: 2   TEXT REFERENCE: 14-3
ANSWER: A

A solar cell with a 30% efficiency rating converts what percent of
the energy it receives from the sun to electrical energy?

A. 30%   C. 40%
B. 70%   D. between 0% and 30%

29) TYPE: M   LEVEL: 1   TEXT REFERENCE: 14-4
ANSWER: D

Ceramics are not:

A. heat resistant.   C. porous.
B. hard.   D. very reactive.

30) TYPE: M   LEVEL: 1   TEXT REFERENCE: 14-4
ANSWER: B

Ceramics contain small crystals of:

A. orthosilicate ion.   C. salts of aluminosilicate.
B. aluminosilicate.   D. salts of orthosilicate ion.

31) TYPE: M   LEVEL: 1   TEXT REFERENCE: 14-5
ANSWER: B

The phenomenon of a light beam being reflected back and forth within
an optical fiber is called:

A. partial internal reflection:
B. total internal reflection.
C. total external reflection.
D. fiber optics.

32) TYPE: M   LEVEL: 2   TEXT REFERENCE: 14-5
ANSWER: D

An optical fiber would be used in:

A. a magnet.   C. human bone replacements.
B. a window.   D. overseas telephone calls.

33) TYPE: M   LEVEL: 2   TEXT REFERENCE: 14-7
ANSWER: A

Which reference would you use to determine who built the first
computer?

A. an encyclopedia
B. a periodical that deals with technical information
C. a periodical dealing with social issues in science
D. your science teacher

34) TYPE: O   LEVEL: 4   TEXT REFERENCE: LA
ANSWER: n

Crystals doped with arsenic atoms having mobile electrons produce
_____- type semiconductors.

35) TYPE: O   LEVEL: 4   TEXT REFERENCE: LA
ANSWER: gallium

A pure silicon crystal doped with _____ results in a
crystal with an electron deficiency.

36) TYPE: O   LEVEL: 4   TEXT REFERENCE: LA
ANSWER: five

A model of the arsenic atom has _____ bored holes.

37) TYPE: O   LEVEL: 4   TEXT REFERENCE: LA
ANSWER: four

A model of the silicon atom has _____ bored holes.

38) TYPE: M   LEVEL: 4   TEXT REFERENCE: LA
ANSWER: C

The structure of a silicon crystal is most similar to the structure
of the molecules in:

A. steel.   C. a diamond.
B. aluminosilicate   D. a magnet.

39) TYPE: M   LEVEL: 4   TEXT REFERENCE: LA
ANSWER: C

The indicator phenolpthalein is used to detect the presence of:

A. H_2O.   C. OH^- ions.
B. Cl^-.   D. none of the above.

40) **TYPE:** M   **LEVEL:** 4   **TEXT REFERENCE:** LA
ANSWER: D

How many bored holes does a model of a Gallium atom have?

A. four   C. five
B. none   D. three

41) **TYPE:** M   **LEVEL:** 4   **TEXT REFERENCE:** LA
ANSWER: A

What type of semiconductors have electron deficiencies?

A. p-type   C. n-type
B. both a and p-types   D. none of the above.

42) **TYPE:** M   **LEVEL:** 4   **TEXT REFERENCE:** LA
ANSWER: B

What is one difference between a pure silicon crystal and an
arsenic-doped crystal?

A. The arsenic-doped crystal has one less electron.
B. The arsenic-doped crystal has one more electron.
C. The arsenic-doped crystal made three bends.
D. none of the above.

43) **TYPE:** M   **LEVEL:** 4   **TEXT REFERENCE:** LA
ANSWER: A

The energy generated by a solar cell may be stored in a:

A. lead storage cell.   C. voltmeter.
B. vacuum tube.   D. none of the above.

44) **TYPE:** M   **LEVEL:** 4   **TEXT REFERENCE:** LA
ANSWER: D

The mass of an integrated circuit is:

A. greater than the mass of a vacuum tube.
B. greater than the mass of a transistor.
C. both A and B.
D. none of the above.

1) TYPE: T   LEVEL: 1   TEXT REFERENCE: 15-1
ANSWER: T

_____   There are no forces of attraction between molecules in an ideal
        gas.

2) TYPE: T   LEVEL: 1   TEXT REFERENCE: 15-2
ANSWER: T

_____   The vapor pressure of a liquid is constant at a constant
        temperature.

3) TYPE: T   LEVEL: 1   TEXT REFERENCE: 15-3
ANSWER: T

_____   The temperature of a boiling liquid is constant at a constant
        temperature.

4) TYPE: T   LEVEL: 1   TEXT REFERENCE: 15-4
ANSWER: T

_____   In order for a solid to melt, energy must be added to the system
        while the temperature remains constant.

5) TYPE: T   LEVEL: 1   TEXT REFERENCE: 15-5
ANSWER: F

_____   The density of the solid form of water is greater than the
        density of the liquid form of water.

6) TYPE: T   LEVEL: 1   TEXT REFERENCE: 15-5
ANSWER: F

_____   The SI temperature unit, kelvin, is defined as the triple point
        of water.

7) TYPE: T   LEVEL: 2   TEXT REFERENCE: 15-7
ANSWER: F

_____   Amorphous solids have relatively low melting points.

8) TYPE: T   LEVEL: 1   TEXT REFERENCE: 15-7
ANSWER: T

_____   The unit cell is the smallest unit that is repeated in three
        dimensions to produce a crystal.

9) TYPE: T   LEVEL: 1   TEXT REFERENCE: 15-9
ANSWER: F

_____   Network solids are good conductors of electricity.

10) TYPE: T   LEVEL: 1   TEXT REFERENCE: 15-10
ANSWER: F

_____   Ionic crystals are good conductors of electricity..

11) TYPE: T   LEVEL: 1   TEXT REFERENCE: 15-11
ANSWER: T

_____   Molecular solids have low melting points.

12) TYPE: T   LEVEL: 1   TEXT REFERENCE: 15-12
ANSWER: F

_____   Substances that release water are called anhydrous
        substances.

13) TYPE: O   LEVEL: 2   TEXT REFERENCE: 15-1
ANSWER: more

Fast-moving molecules have _____ kinetic energy than
slow-moving molecules.

14) TYPE: O   LEVEL: 1   TEXT REFERENCE: 15-2
ANSWER: manometer

The pressure of a gas in a closed evacuated container can be measured
using a(n) _____.

15) TYPE: O   LEVEL: 1   TEXT REFERENCE: 15-2
ANSWER: volatile

A substance whose molecules evaporate readily is said to be
_____.

16) TYPE: O   LEVEL: 2   TEXT REFERENCE: 15-2
ANSWER: condensation.

The processes that are in balance between a liquid and a vapor at
equilibrium are evaporation and _____.

17) TYPE: O   LEVEL: 1   TEXT REFERENCE: 15-2
ANSWER: sublimation

The process of a solid changing directly to a vapor without first forming a liquid is called _____.

18) TYPE: O   LEVEL: 1   TEXT REFERENCE: 15-4
ANSWER: crystalline

The molecules of a solid arranged in an orderly pattern are described by the word _____.

19) TYPE: O   LEVEL: 1   TEXT REFERENCE: 15-5
ANSWER: triple

The _____ point of a substance shows the temperature and pressure at which the substance exists simultaneously as a solid, liquid, and gas.

20) TYPE: O   LEVEL: 1   TEXT REFERENCE: 15-6
ANSWER: wetting

Surface tension helps determine how well a liquid functions as a(n) _____ agent.

21) TYPE: O   LEVEL: 1   TEXT REFERENCE: 15-7
ANSWER: amorphous

Solids that do not have a crystalline structure are called _____ solids.

22) TYPE: O   LEVEL: 1   TEXT REFERENCE: 15-8
ANSWER: alloys

Metals may be melted and mixed together in varying proportions to form _____.

23) TYPE: O   LEVEL: 1   TEXT REFERENCE: 15-9
ANSWER: network

A solid with a web of covalent bonds in a three-dimensional structure is a(n) _____ solid.

24) TYPE: O   LEVEL: 1   TEXT REFERENCE: 15-11
ANSWER: molecular

A solid composed of molecules made of a few atoms joined together by covalent bonds is called a(n) _____ solid.

Chapter 15 THE CONDENSED STATES OF MATTER

25) **TYPE:** O   **LEVEL:** 1   **TEXT REFERENCE:** 15-12
ANSWER: hydrate

A solid crystal resulting from the evaporation of water from a solution is called a _____.

26) **TYPE:** O   **LEVEL:** 2   **TEXT REFERENCE:** 15-12
ANSWER: anhydrous

The dehydration of zinc sulfate pentahydrate would reult in a solid called _____ zinc sulfate.

27) **TYPE:** M   **LEVEL:** 2   **TEXT REFERENCE:** 15-1
ANSWER: B

Which of the following is not characteristic of a gas?

A. The molecules are in constant motion.
B. The molecules are strongly attracted to each other.
C. In a gas sample there are different kinetic energies.
D. A gas completely fills its container.

28) **TYPE:** M   **LEVEL:** 2   **TEXT REFERENCE:** 15-2
ANSWER: A

In a container with a liquid and some vapor, an increase in the number of molecules in the vapor phase means that the chance of a molecule moving into the liquid phase:

A. increases.   C. stays the same.
B. decreases.   D. cannot tell.

29) **TYPE:** M   **LEVEL:** 2   **TEXT REFERENCE:** 15-2
ANSWER: A

If the vapor pressure of Glogg is 0.125 atm at 25° C, and the vapor pressure of Axorf is 0.035 atm at 25° C, which has the greater tendency to evaporate?

A. Glogg   C. both the same
B. Axorf   D. cannot tell

30) **TYPE:** M   **LEVEL:** 2   **TEXT REFERENCE:** 15-2
ANSWER: B

If the temperature in a desert is the same as the temperature in a tropical rain forest, which climate will feel hotter to your skin?

A. desert   B. both will feel the same
B. rain forest   D. cannot tell

31) TYPE: M   LEVEL: 2   TEXT REFERENCE: 15-3
ANSWER: C

A boiling liquid will have:

A. increasing average kinetic energy.
B. decreasing average kinetic energy.
C. constant temperature.
D. increasing temperature.

32) TYPE: M   LEVEL: 1   TEXT REFERENCE: 15-4
ANSWER: C

During the melting process, the temperature of the solid is:

A. less than the temperature of the liquid.
B. greater than the temperature of the liquid.
C. the same as the temperature of the liquid.
D. variable in relation to the temperature of the liquid.

33) TYPE: M   LEVEL: 2   TEXT REFERENCE: 15-4
ANSWER: D

On a graph of time vs. temperature for the heating of various
substances, the plateaus show the:

A. boiling temperatures.   C. pressure points.
B. melting temperatures.   D. both A and B

34) TYPE: M   LEVEL: 1   TEXT REFERENCE: 15-5
ANSWER: C

The relationships among pressure, temperature, and the phase of a
substance can be summarized by a:

A. pressure diagram.   C. phase diagram.
B. temperature diagram.   D. closed-system diagram.

35) TYPE: M   LEVEL: 2   TEXT REFERENCE: 15-6
ANSWER: A

Adding soap to water will:

A. make water a better wetting agent.
B. increase the surface tension of the water.
C. make water a less effective wetting agent.
D. not affect the adhesive forces of water.

Chapter 15   THE CONDENSED STATES OF MATTER

36) TYPE: M   LEVEL: 2   TEXT REFERENCE: 15-9
ANSWER: C

Which of the following is not a characteristic of a network solid?

A. They are covalently bonded.
B. They are among the hardest substances known.
C. They have low melting points.
D. They form a three-dimensional crystal.

37) TYPE: M   LEVEL: 2   TEXT REFERENCE: 15-10
ANSWER: D

A crystal composed of alternating positive and negative ions in a
three-dimensional arrangement would be called:

A. a metal.   C. a network solid.
B. an alloy.   D. an ionic solid.

38) TYPE: M   LEVEL: 2   TEXT REFERENCE: 15-10
ANSWER: A

The ratio of positive to negative ions in potassium chloride is:

A. 1/1.   C. 2/1.
B. 1/2.   D. cannot tell.

39) TYPE: M   LEVEL: 2   TEXT REFERENCE: 15-11
ANSWER: C

Molecular solids with large masses:

A. have very high melting points.
B. are held together with covalent bonds.
C. are solids at room temperature.
D. none of the above.

40) TYPE: M   LEVEL: 2   TEXT REFERENCE: 15-12
ANSWER: D

The correct formula for magnesium chloride hexahydrate is:

A. 6 $MgCl_2$.   C. $MgCl_2(H_2O)_6$.
B. $MgCl_2 \times 6H_2O$.   D. none of these.

41) TYPE: M   LEVEL: 2   TEXT REFERENCE: 15-12
ANSWER: B

The process that produces an anhydrous substance can be reversed by:

A. taking out water.   C. heating the substance.
B. adding water.   D. none of the above.

42) TYPE: M   LEVEL: 4   TEXT REFERENCE: LA
ANSWER: C

Which of the following liquids at the same temperature will feel
coolest to the touch?

A. water   C. acetone
B. 2-propanol   D. all feel the same

43) TYPE: M   LEVEL: 4   TEXT REFERENCE: LA
ANSWER: A

At 25° C, which of the following liquids has the greatest vapor
pressure?

A. acetone   C. 2-propanol
B. water   D. all are the same

44) TYPE: M   LEVEL: 4   TEXT REFERENCE: LA
ANSWER: C

Which of the following liquids has the greatest attractive forces
between molecules?

A. acetone   C. water
B. 2-propanol   D. all are the same

45) TYPE: M   LEVEL: 4   TEXT REFERENCE: LA
ANSWER: A

Which of the following liquids has the greatest surface tension?

A. water   C. 0.1% detergent solution
B. 5% detergent solution   D. all are the same

46) TYPE: M   LEVEL: 4   TEXT REFERENCE: LB
ANSWER: D

The maximum number of spheres of one size that can contact a central
sphere is:

A. four   C. eight
B. six   D. twelve

47) TYPE: M   LEVEL: 4   TEXT REFERENCE: LB
ANSWER: B

In what type of cubic packing do the spheres occupy two-thirds of the
total space?

A. face-centered cubic   C. orbit-centered cubic
B. body-centered cubic   D. hexagonal closest packed

48) TYPE: M   LEVEL: 4   TEXT REFERENCE: LB
ANSWER: A

What type of cubic packing is the most dense?

A. face-centered cubic   C. orbit-centered cubic
B. body-centered cubic   D. none of the above

49) TYPE: M   LEVEL: 4   TEXT REFERENCE: LB
ANSWER: B

What is the coordination number of iron in its stable form, the
face-centered cubic?

A. -ferrite = 0   C. -ferrite = 8
B. -ferrite = 12   D. -ferrite = 4

50) TYPE: M   LEVEL: 4   TEXT REFERENCE: LB
ANSWER: C

The high density sodium chloride crystal is stable because:

A. it contains mobile electrons.
B. it contains many valence electrons.
C. of the attractive forces between oppositely charged ions.
D. of the repulsive forces between oppositely charged ions.

51) TYPE: M   LEVEL: 4   TEXT REFERENCE: LB
ANSWER: D

In a sodium chloride crystal, how many chloride ions surround a sodium
ion?

A. none   C. eight
B. twelve   D. six

Chapter 16 SOLUTIONS

1) TYPE: T   LEVEL: 2   TEXT REFERENCE: 16-1
ANSWER: T

____ Seawater is a homogeneous mixture.

2) TYPE: T   LEVEL: 2   TEXT REFERENCE: 16-1
ANSWER: F

____ In a 15% alcohol solution, water is the solute and alcohol is
      the solvent.

3) TYPE: T   LEVEL: 1   TEXT REFERENCE: 16-2
ANSWER: T

____ In a solution, temperature influences how much solid will
      dissolve and how fast it will dissolve.

4) TYPE: T   LEVEL: 2   TEXT REFERENCE: 16-3
ANSWER: T

____ A teaspoonful of salt will dissociate in a gallon of water.

5) TYPE: T   LEVEL: 1   TEXT REFERENCE: 16-4
ANSWER: F

____ If polar and nonpolar substances are mixed, they demonstrate a
      strong attraction for each other.

6) TYPE: T   LEVEL: 3   TEXT REFERENCE: 16-5
ANSWER: T

____ The molality of a solution is obtained by dividing the moles of
      solute by the kilograms of solvent.

7) TYPE: T   LEVEL: 1   TEXT REFERENCE: 16-6
ANSWER: F

____ Supersaturated solutions are very stable.

8) TYPE: T   LEVEL: 1   TEXT REFERENCE: 16-7
ANSWER: T

____ Henry's law states: The mass of a gas solute dissolved within a
      liquid is proportional to the pressure upon the system.

9) TYPE: T   LEVEL: 2   TEXT REFERENCE: 16-10
ANSWER: T

_____   The additon of a nonvolatile solute to a solution will raise
        the boiling point of the solution.

10) TYPE: T   LEVEL: 1   TEXT REFERENCE: 16-11
ANSWER: T

_____   Distillation is a technique used to produce a solute-free
        liquid.

11) TYPE: T   LEVEL: 2   TEXT REFERENCE: 16-12
ANSWER: F

_____   The nonvolatile liquid ethylene glycol is used as an antifreeze
        because it causes the colligative effect known as freezing point
        elevation.

12) TYPE: T   LEVEL: 1   TEXT REFERENCE: 16-13
ANSWER: F

_____   Any negative ion plus the ammonium ion will form an ionic
        compound that is insoluble in water.

13) TYPE: T   LEVEL: 1   TEXT REFERENCE: 16-14
ANSWER: T

_____   One limitation of net ionic equations is that it is possible to
        oversimplify an equation.

14) TYPE: T   LEVEL: 2   TEXT REFERENCE: 16-15
ANSWER: F

_____   A solute to solvent ratio of one part to one-million parts
        indicates a very high solubility.

15) TYPE: O   LEVEL: 1   TEXT REFERENCE: 16-1
ANSWER: heterogeneous

Mixtures characterized by an observable segregation of component
substances are called _____ mixtures.

16) TYPE: O   LEVEL: 1   TEXT REFERENCE: 16-1
ANSWER: solvent

Within a homogeneous mixture or solution, the substance present in
the greater quantity is known as the _____ .

17) **TYPE:** O   **LEVEL:** 2   **TEXT REFERENCE:** 16-1
ANSWER: solute

In an 85% alcohol solution, water is the _____.

18) **TYPE:** O   **LEVEL:** 1   **TEXT REFERENCE:** 16-2
ANSWER: unsaturated

Solutions that are able to dissolve additional solute are said to be
_____.

19) **TYPE:** O   **LEVEL:** 1   **TEXT REFERENCE:** 16-2
ANSWER: immiscible

Substances that are insoluble in each other are called
_____.

20) **TYPE:** O   **LEVEL:** 1   **TEXT REFERENCE:** 16-3
ANSWER: solvation

The interaction between solute and solvent particles resulting in a
solution is called _____.

21) **TYPE:** O   **LEVEL:** 1   **TEXT REFERENCE:** 16-3
ANSWER: dissociation

The process of crystal decomposition into component ions is called
_____.

22) **TYPE:** O   **LEVEL:** 3   **TEXT REFERENCE:** 16-5
ANSWER: solute, solvent

Molality is obtained by dividing the moles of _____ by
the kilograms of _____.

23) **TYPE:** O   **LEVEL:** 1   **TEXT REFERENCE:** 16-6
ANSWER: supersaturated

Solutions containing more solute than can normally be dissolved at a
given temperature are known as _____.

24) **TYPE:** O   **LEVEL:** 1   **TEXT REFERENCE:** 16-8
ANSWER: solution

The change in energy associated with solvation is called the heat of
_____.

25) **TYPE:** O   **LEVEL:** 1   **TEXT REFERENCE:** 16-9
ANSWER: colligative

Properties that are independent of solute identity are known as
_____ properties.

26) **TYPE:** O   **LEVEL:** 1   **TEXT REFERENCE:** 16-10
ANSWER: elevation

The addition of NaCl to a beaker of water will cause an effect known
as the boiling point _____.

27) **TYPE:** O   **LEVEL:** 1   **TEXT REFERENCE:** 16-11
ANSWER: distillation

Chemists use a procedure known as fractional _____ to
separate solution fractions of similar vapor pressures.

28) **TYPE:** O   **LEVEL:** 1   **TEXT REFERENCE:** 16-13
ANSWER: spectator

Ions that do not participate in a reaction are called
_____ ions.

29) **TYPE:** O   **LEVEL:** 1   **TEXT REFERENCE:** 16-15
ANSWER: K_{sp}

The solubility product constant is abbreviated _____.

30) **TYPE:** M   **LEVEL:** 2   **TEXT REFERENCE:** 16-1
ANSWER: C

Which of the following is an aqueous solution?

A. air   C. blood
B. an 80% alcohol solution   D. a dental filling

31) **TYPE:** M   **LEVEL:** 2   **TEXT REFERENCE:** 16-2
ANSWER: B

If a small amount of sugar is added to a solution and it dissolves,
the original solution was:

A. saturated.   C. immiscible.
B. unsaturated.   D. heterogeneous.

32) TYPE: M   LEVEL: 2   TEXT REFERENCE: 16-2
ANSWER: A

Two nonpolar substances are most likely:

A. miscible.   C. immiscible.
B. saturated.   D. cannot tell.

33) TYPE: M   LEVEL: 2   TEXT REFERENCE: 16-3
ANSWER: A

The dissociation of a small amount of sugar would be best accomplished
by adding it to:

A. a cup of coffee.
B. a teaspoonful of maple syrup.
C. a gallon of cooking oil.
D. none of the above.

34) TYPE: M   LEVEL: 2   TEXT REFERENCE: 16-3
ANSWER: D

If an ionic solid is mixed with a nonpolar solvent, which of the
following is most likely to occur?

A. solvation   C. dissociation
B. saturation   D. none of the above

35) TYPE: M   LEVEL: 2   TEXT REFERENCE: 16-4
ANSWER: B

Which of the following is a mixture in which solvation occurs?

A. oil and vinegar   C. motor oil and water
B. water and ethanol   D. none of the above

36) TYPE: M   LEVEL: 3   TEXT REFERENCE: 16-5
ANSWER: A

What is the molality of a solution containg 300 g of H_2O_2
dissolved in 2000 cm^3 of water?

A. 4.4m solution   C. 2.2m solution
B. 8.8m solution   D. none of the above

37) TYPE: M   LEVEL: 3   TEXT REFERENCE: 16-5
ANSWER: B

How many grams of NaCl would you mix with 1000 g of water to prepare
a 0.5m solution?

A. 15 g NaCl   C. 1.5 g NaCl
B. 29.3 g NaCl   D. 2.93 g NaCl

38) TYPE: M   LEVEL: 1   TEXT REFERENCE: 16-6
ANSWER: C

Solutions that are capable of supporting more solute than can usually
be dissolved are called:

A. saturated.   C. supersaturated.
B. unsaturated.   D. miscible

39) TYPE: M   LEVEL: 2   TEXT REFERENCE: 16-7
ANSWER: B

According to Henry's law, when a gas/liquid solution is heated, the
gas solubility:

A. increases.   C. stays the same.
B. decreases.   D. doubles.

40) TYPE: M   LEVEL: 1   TEXT REFERENCE: 16-8
ANSWER: A

The tendency in nature that determines physical and chemical
reactability is the tendency toward:

A. maximum disorder.   C. minimum disorder.
B. maximum energy.   D. none of the above.

41) TYPE: M   LEVEL: 1   TEXT REFERENCE: 16-9
ANSWER: D

Which of the following are colligative properties?

A. vapor pressure   C. boiling point
B. osmotic pressure   D. all of the above

42) TYPE: M   LEVEL: 1   TEXT REFERENCE: 16-10
ANSWER: B

In a solution, the effect known as the boiling point elevation is
caused by the addition of:

A. a volatile solute.   C. a volatile solvent.
B. a nonvolatile solute.   D. a nonvolatile solvent.

43) TYPE: M   LEVEL: 2   TEXT REFERENCE: 16-11
ANSWER: B

The process that would most likely be used to separate the components
of crude oil is:

A. distillation.   C. boiling point elevation.
B. fractional distillation.   D. freezing point depression.

44) TYPE: M   LEVEL: 2   TEXT REFERENCE: 16-12
ANSWER: A

The addition of salt to a beaker of water will result in a
colligative effect known as:

A. freezing point   C. boiling point
   depression.   depression.
B. freezing point   D. none of the above.
   elevation.

45) TYPE: M   LEVEL: 1   TEXT REFERENCE: 16-13
ANSWER: D

Any anion will form an ionic compound that is soluble in water when
combined with:

A. any cation.   C. nitrate.
B. any cation except Ag^+.   D. alkali metal ions like Na^+.

46) TYPE: M   LEVEL: 2   TEXT REFERENCE: 16-13
ANSWER: D

The net ionic equation for the following reaction is:
$Na^+(aq) + OH^-(aq) + H^+(aq) + Cl^-(aq) \rightarrow$
$$Na^+(aq) + Cl^-(aq) + HOH\ (l)$$

A. $Na^+(aq) + Cl^-(aq) \rightarrow NaCl$
B. $Na^+(aq) + OH^-(aq) \rightarrow NaOH$
C. $OH^-(aq) + H^+(aq) \rightarrow H_2O$
D. $OH^-(aq) + H^+(aq) \rightarrow HOH(l)$

47) TYPE: M   LEVEL: 2   TEXT REFERENCE: 16-15
ANSWER: D

What is the solubility product expression for $CaSO_4$

A. $[Ca][SO_4]$ C. $[Ca^{2+}][SO_4]$
B. $[Ca^{2-}][SO_4]$ D. $[Ca^{2+}][SO_4^{2-}]$

48) TYPE: M   LEVEL: 2   TEXT REFERENCE: 16-15
ANSWER: A

What is the solubility product constant of AgBr if the $[Br^-]$ dissolved in water is 5.0×10^{-5}?

A. 2.5×10^{-9} C. 2.5×10^{-10}
B. 1.0×10^{-9} D. 1.0×10^{-10}

49) TYPE: M   LEVEL: 2   TEXT REFERENCE: 16-15
ANSWER: B

How much $BaSO_4$ will dissolve in 1 liter of water if the solubility product constant is 1.5×10^{-5}?

A. 2.25×10^{-10} moles per liter
B. 3.87×10^{-3} moles per liter
C. 3.0×10^{-5} moles per liter
D. 0.39×10^{-3} moles per liter

50) TYPE: M   LEVEL: 2   TEXT REFERENCE: 16-15
ANSWER: C

Which of the following compounds is the most soluble in water?

A. AgI (solubility product constant = 8.5×10^{-17})
B. AgBr (solubility product constant = 5.0×10^{-13})
C. AgCl (solubility product constant = 1.7×10^{-10})
D. Ag_2S (solubility product constant = 6.3×10^{-50})

51) TYPE: O   LEVEL: 4   TEXT REFERENCE: LB
ANSWER: decreases

For molecular solutes, as the molality increases, the freezing point
_____.

52) TYPE: O   LEVEL: 4   TEXT REFERENCE: LB
ANSWER: decreases

For ionic solutes, as the number of ions in solution increases, the freezing point _____.

53) TYPE: M   LEVEL: 4   TEXT REFERENCE: LA
ANSWER: A

In which of the following will one tablespoon of sugar dissolve the
fastest?

A. a cup of coffee
B. a glass of iced tea
C. a glass of water at room temperature
D. all the same

54) TYPE: M   LEVEL: 4   TEXT REFERENCE: LA
ANSWER: A

Dissolved solid molecules or ions in a solution move:

A. faster than dissolved gas molecules.
B. slower than dissolved gas molecules.
C. at the same rate as gas molecules.
D. cannot tell.

55) TYPE: M   LEVEL: 4   TEXT REFERENCE: LA
ANSWER: B

Which of the following will be least effective in increasing the
solubility of a solid in a liquid?

A. An increase in temperature.
B. An increase in pressure.
C. Stirring the solution.
D. Crushing the solid particles.

56) TYPE: M   LEVEL: 4   TEXT REFERENCE: LA
ANSWER: A

Which of the following solids is most soluble at 100° C?

A. potassium nitrate
B. sodium chloride
C. large crystals of sodium choride
D. cannot tell

57) TYPE: M   LEVEL: 4   TEXT REFERENCE: LA
ANSWER: C

Which expression desribes the same solubility as 6 grams of KNO_3 in
20 mL of hot water?

A. 2 g/40 mL   C. 12 g/40 mL
B. 0.5 g/40 mL   D. 24 g/40 mL

Chapter 16   SOLUTIONS

58) TYPE: M   LEVEL: 4   TEXT REFERENCE: LB
ANSWER: B

If the K_f for water is $1.86°$ C/m, a 1m solution containing a molecular solute freezes at:

A. $1.86°$ C.
B. $1.86°$ C below the freezing point of water.
C. $1.86°$ C above the freezing point of water.
D. $3.72°$ C below the freezing point of water.

59) TYPE: M   LEVEL: 4   TEXT REFERENCE: LB
ANSWER: D

If the K_f for water is $1.86°$C/m, a 1m solution containing the ionic solute NaCl freezes at:

A. $1.86°$ C.
B. $1.86°$ C below the freezing point of water.
C. $3.72°$ C above the freezing point of water.
D. $3.72°$ C below the freezing point of water.

60) TYPE: M   LEVEL: 4   TEXT REFERENCE: LC
ANSWER: C

What is the Pb^{2+} ion concentration in a saturated solution of $PbCl_2$ if an accepted K_{sp} value is 1.0×10^{-4}?

A. 25×10^{-6}
B. 4×10^{-6}
C. 2.9×10^{-2}
D. 2.9×10^{-6}

61) TYPE: M   LEVEL: 4   TEXT REFERENCE: LC
ANSWER: A

Complete the balanced equation for the following double replacement reaction:
$$Sr(OH)_2(aq) + Na_2CO_3(aq) \rightarrow$$

A. $SrCO_3(s) + 2Na^+(aq) + 2OH^-(aq)$
B. $SrCO_3(s) + Na^+(aq) + OH^-(aq)$
C. $Sr^{2+}(aq) + CO_3^{2-}(aq) + 2NaOH(s)$
D. $2SrCO_3(s) + NaOH(aq)$

Chapter 17   THERMODYNAMICS

1) TYPE: T   LEVEL: 1   TEXT REFERENCE: 17-1
ANSWER: F

_____   Temperature is expressed as a unitary rate.

2) TYPE: T   LEVEL: 2   TEXT REFERENCE: 17-1
ANSWER: F

_____   There is more heat in an iceberg than in a cup of boiling water
        because the average energy of the water molecules in the iceberg
        is greater than of those in the boiling water.

3) TYPE: T   LEVEL: 1   TEXT REFERENCE: 17-2
ANSWER: T

_____   Specific heat is expressed as a double unitary rate.

4) TYPE: T   LEVEL: 2   TEXT REFERENCE: 17-3
ANSWER: T

_____   Both the heat of fusion and the heat of vaporization depend on
        the amount of material that is changed.

5) TYPE: T   LEVEL: 2   TEXT REFERENCE: 17-3
ANSWER: F

_____   The heat of vaporization describes the temperature change that
        causes cold water to become warm as it is heated.

6) TYPE: T   LEVEL: 1   TEXT REFERENCE: 17-5
ANSWER: F

_____   A kilocalorie is one hundred times larger than a calorie.

7) TYPE: T   LEVEL: 1   TEXT REFERENCE: 17-5
ANSWER: F

_____   A kilocalorie is the unit most commonly used by scientists to
        describe energy.

8) TYPE: T   LEVEL: 1   TEXT REFERENCE: 17-6
ANSWER: T

_____   The word "calorimeter" literally means "heat measurer."

9) TYPE: T   LEVEL: 1   TEXT REFERENCE: 17-7
ANSWER: T

_____   When any chemical bond forms, the reaction that caused it is
said to be exothermic.

10) TYPE: T   LEVEL: 1   TEXT REFERENCE: 17-8
ANSWER: F

_____   An endothermic reaction is indicated by a negative sign in
front of the standard heat of formation value.

11) TYPE: T   LEVEL: 2   TEXT REFERENCE: 17-10
ANSWER: F

_____   Burning a cookie in a calorimeter will accurately tell how much
energy will be provided to the body if the cookie is digested.

12) TYPE: T   LEVEL: 1   TEXT REFERENCE: 17-11
ANSWER: F

_____   The body utilizes all of the available energy supplied by food.

13) TYPE: T   LEVEL: 1   TEXT REFERENCE: 17-12
ANSWER: F

_____   The free energy of a system is represented by the symbol
delta-D.

14) TYPE: T   LEVEL: 1   TEXT REFERENCE: 17-12
ANSWER: T

_____   The delta-G for any spontaneous reaction will be negative.

15) TYPE: O   LEVEL: 1   TEXT REFERENCE: 17-1
ANSWER: thermodynamics

The study of energy transformations is referred to as

_____.

16) TYPE: O   LEVEL: 1   TEXT REFERENCE: 17-1
ANSWER: molecule

Temperature describes the amount of heat per _____ of a
substance.

17) TYPE: O   LEVEL: 1   TEXT REFERENCE: 17-3
ANSWER: fusion

The energy required to change one kilogram of a substance from solid
to liquid is the heat of _____.

18) TYPE: O   LEVEL: 1   TEXT REFERENCE: 17-5
ANSWER: Calorie

One kilocalorie is commonly known as one _____.

19) TYPE: O   LEVEL: 1   TEXT REFERENCE: 17-5
ANSWER: 4.184

One calorie is equal to _____ joules.

20) TYPE: O   LEVEL: 1   TEXT REFERENCE: 17-6
ANSWER: calorimeter

A container in which heat measurements are made is called a(n)
_____.

21) TYPE: O   LEVEL: 1   TEXT REFERENCE: 17-7
ANSWER: sun

The primary source of energy used on Earth is the _____.

22) TYPE: O   LEVEL: 1   TEXT REFERENCE: 17-8
ANSWER: standard

The set of conditions under which you would normally find an element
is known as its _____ state.

23) TYPE: O   LEVEL: 1   TEXT REFERENCE: 17-8
ANSWER: reaction

Energy observed during a chemical change is called the heat of
_____.

24) TYPE: O   LEVEL: 1   TEXT REFERENCE: 17-8
ANSWER: enthalpy

The term used to describe the heat measured when changes takes place
at a constant pressure is _____.

25) **TYPE:** O   **LEVEL:** 1   **TEXT REFERENCE:** 17-10
ANSWER: four

When sugars burn to produce carbon dioxide and water they release about _____ Calories of energy per gram of sugar.

26) **TYPE:** O   **LEVEL:** 1   **TEXT REFERENCE:** 17-10
ANSWER: combustion

The total energy released when a substance is burned is called the heat of _____.

27) **TYPE:** O   **LEVEL:** 1   **TEXT REFERENCE:** 17-11
ANSWER: exothermic

In order to get useful work from a reaction it must be both spontaneous and _____.

28) **TYPE:** O   **LEVEL:** 1   **TEXT REFERENCE:** 17-12
ANSWER: Gibbs

The maximum possible work obtained from a reaction is called the _____ Free Energy.

29) **TYPE:** O   **LEVEL:** 1   **TEXT REFERENCE:** 17-13
ANSWER: entropy

The way in which energy is distributed in a system is described by the term _____.

30) **TYPE:** M   **LEVEL:** 1   **TEXT REFERENCE:** 17-1
ANSWER: C

The assumption that is made when you use a thermometer is that two objects placed in contact will gain or lose heat until their temperatures:

A. become hotter.
B. become colder.
C. are equal.
D. expand the materials in the thermometer.

31) TYPE: M   LEVEL: 1   TEXT REFERENCE: 17-2
ANSWER: D

The specific heat is the energy in joules required to raise the temperature of one:

A. mole of material one kelvin.
B. gram of material one kelvin.
C. mole of material one degree Celsius.
D. kilogram of material one kelvin or one degree Celsius.

32) TYPE: M   LEVEL: 2   TEXT REFERENCE: 17-2
ANSWER: B

Which of the following would not be a good characteristic of material to be used for heat storage in a solar home?

A. is inexpensive   C. heats up slowly
B. cools down fast   D. has a high specific heat

33) TYPE: M   LEVEL: 2   TEXT REFERENCE: 17-2
ANSWER: A

How much iron (specific heat = 473 joules per kilogram kelvin) is needed to store 100,000 kilojoules of heat when its temperature changes by 10K?

A. 2.11×10^4 kg   C. 2.11×10^{-4} kg
B. 4.7×10^{-1} kg   D. 4.7×10^{-1} m^3

34) TYPE: M   LEVEL: 1   TEXT REFERENCE: 17-3
ANSWER: C

The heat of vaporization is the energy required to change one kilogram of a substance from a:

A. solid to gas.   C. liquid to a gas.
B. solid to liquid.   D. gas to liquid.

35) TYPE: M   LEVEL: 1   TEXT REFERENCE: 17-3
ANSWER: C

Farmers protect their crops from severe frost damage by spraying them with water because:

A. the water raises the temperature of the surrounding air.
B. the freezing water absorbs heat from the plants.
C. the ice that coats the crops protects them from the colder air.
D. both A and C.

36) TYPE: M   LEVEL: 2   TEXT REFERENCE: 17-3
ANSWER: A

Energy can be stored by:

A. changing a substance to   C. condensing a substance.
   a gas.
B. freezing a substance.   D. cooling a substance.

37) TYPE: M   LEVEL: 2   TEXT REFERENCE: 17-4
ANSWER: B

When rapidly-moving molecules escape from a liquid in evaporation,
the average speed of the molecules left behind is:

A. higher than before the evaporation.
B. lower than before the evaporation.
C. the same as before the evaporation.
D. twice as great as before the evaporation.

38) TYPE: M   LEVEL: 2   TEXT REFERENCE: 17-4
ANSWER: C

As the wax in a candle melts, the heat of fusion is responsible for:

A. the burning of the wick.
B. the wax becoming hot.
C. the melting of the wax.
D. the smoke from the wick.

39) TYPE: M   LEVEL: 1   TEXT REFERENCE: 17-5
ANSWER: B

The energy required to raise the temperature of one gram of water one
Celsius degree is defined as one:

A. Calorie.   C. kilocalorie.
B. calorie.   D. kelvin.

40) TYPE: M   LEVEL: 1   TEXT REFERENCE: 17-5
ANSWER: A

One calorie is equal to:

A. 4.184 joules.   C. 4184 joules.
B. one Calorie.   D. one joule.

41) TYPE: M   LEVEL: 2   TEXT REFERENCE: 17-5
ANSWER: B

One slice of bread that contains 150 Calories contains:

A. 27.9 Joules.   C. 627.6 Joules
B. 627 600 joules.   D. 0.0278 joules.

42) TYPE: M   LEVEL: 2   TEXT REFERENCE: 17-6
ANSWER: B

A good calorimeter is not:

A. well-insulated.
B. responsive to changes in pressure.
C. responsive to changes in temperature.
D. made of thick plastic foam.

43) TYPE: M   LEVEL: 1   TEXT REFERENCE: 17-7
ANSWER: A

Photosynthesis is:

A. an endothermic reaction.   C. neither A nor B.
B. an exothermic reaction.   D. both A and B.

44) TYPE: M   LEVEL: 1   TEXT REFERENCE: 17-8
ANSWER: D

The standard state of an element involves a particular:

A. temperature and pressure only.
B. temperature and physical state only.
C. pressure and physical state only.
D. temperature, pressure, and physical state.

45) TYPE: M   LEVEL: 1   TEXT REFERENCE: 17-8
ANSWER: A

The symbol for enthalpy is:

A. H
B. S
C. the same symbol used to represent "delta."
D. the superscript o.

46) TYPE: M   LEVEL: 2   TEXT REFERENCE: 17-8
ANSWER: B

The energy value delta-H = -456.3 kJ indicates that the reaction is:

A. endothermic.   C. neither A nor B.
B. exothermic.   D. cannot tell.

47) TYPE: M   LEVEL: 1   TEXT REFERENCE: 17-10
ANSWER: A

The energy released when a substance is burned is called the:

A. heat of combustion.   C. heat of formation.
B. heat of reaction.   D. enthalpy.

48) TYPE: M   LEVEL: 1   TEXT REFERENCE: 17-11
ANSWER: D

In order to get useful work from a chemical reaction it must not:

A. proceed spontaneously.
B. be exothermic.
C. provide energy in a useful form.
D. need an energy supply.

49) TYPE: M   LEVEL: 1   TEXT REFERENCE: 17-12
ANSWER: A

The maximum amount of work that can be done by a chemical reaction is
represented by:

A. delta-G.   C. H.
B. delta-H.   D. the subscript f.

50) TYPE: M   LEVEL: 2   TEXT REFERENCE: 17-12
ANSWER: B

If the change in free energy for a reaction is negative, the:

A. reaction can not occur spontaneously.
B. reaction can occur spontaneously.
C. reverse reaction can occur spontaneously.
D. chemical system is in equilibrium.

51) TYPE: M   LEVEL: 1   TEXT REFERENCE: 17-13
ANSWER: B

The symbol for entropy is:

A. H.   C. G.
B. S.   D. E.

52) TYPE: O   LEVEL: 4   TEXT REFERENCE: LA
ANSWER: exothermic

A negative value for H indicates a(n) _____ reaction.

53) TYPE: O   LEVEL: 4   TEXT REFERENCE: LB
ANSWER: 3.34 × 10^5

The heat of fusion of water is _____ J/kg.

54) TYPE: M   LEVEL: 4   TEXT REFERENCE: LA
ANSWER: C

If the products of a reaction contain a lower enthalpy than their
reactants, the reaction is said to be:

A. endothermic.   C. exothermic.
B. neither A nor B.   D. cannot tell.

55) TYPE: M   LEVEL: 4   TEXT REFERENCE: LA
ANSWER: A

In a reaction between NaOH and H_2O, if the amount of NaOH used is
doubled, the amount of heat released:

A. will double.
B. remains the same.
C. will be half as much.
D. will be four times as much.

56) TYPE: M   LEVEL: 4   TEXT REFERENCE: LA
ANSWER: B

The reaction that takes place inside a "cold pack" when it is used to
treat athletic injuries is:

A. exothermic.   C. neither A nor B.
B. endothermic.   D. cannot tell.

57) TYPE: M   LEVEL: 4   TEXT REFERENCE: LB
ANSWER: A

If you drop a cube of ice into a glass of water that is at room
temperature, where does the heat come from that causes the ice cube
to melt?

A. the water   C. the glass
B. the air   D. inside the ice

58) TYPE: M   LEVEL: 4   TEXT REFERENCE: LB
ANSWER: C

In order to calculate the energy absorbed by a mass of melted ice,
you must know the:

A. mass of water, final temperature, specific heat of ice.
B. mass of water, specific heat of ice.
C. mass of ice, final temperature, specific heat of water.
D. mass of ice, specific heat of water.

59) TYPE: M   LEVEL: 4   TEXT REFERENCE: LB
ANSWER: D

In order to calculate the heat of fusion for a mass of ice in water,
you must know the:

A. energy absorbed by water, mass of water.
B. energy absorbed by water, mass of ice.
C. energy absorbed by ice, mass of water.
D. energy abosrbed by ice, mass of ice.

1) TYPE: T   LEVEL: 1   TEXT REFERENCE: 18-2
ANSWER: F

____ The rate of a chemical reaction increases as the concentration
of reactants decreases.

2) TYPE: T   LEVEL: 2   TEXT REFERENCE: 18-2
ANSWER: F

____ The rate of a chemical reaction does not depend upon the
concentrations of the reactants.

3) TYPE: T   LEVEL: 1   TEXT REFERENCE: 18-3
ANSWER: T

____ Increasing the surface area where a reaction takes place will
increase the reaction rate.

4) TYPE: T   LEVEL: 2   TEXT REFERENCE: 18-3
ANSWER: T

____ Cutting a solid reactant into smaller pieces will increase the
reaction rate.

5) TYPE: T   LEVEL: 1   TEXT REFERENCE: 18-4
ANSWER: F

____ In order for a chemical reaction to occur, each reacting
molecule must have energy at least equal to the threshold
energy.

6) TYPE: T   LEVEL: 1   TEXT REFERENCE: 18-4
ANSWER: T

____ Chemical reactions are caused by high-energy molecular
collisons.

7) TYPE: T   LEVEL: 1   TEXT REFERENCE: 18-5
ANSWER: T

____ The activation energy can be considered to be the same as the
minimum threshold energy.

8) TYPE: T   LEVEL: 1   TEXT REFERENCE: 18-5
ANSWER: F

_____ The activated complex is a "molecule" at the top of the energy
barrier that has a relatively long lifetime.

9) TYPE: T   LEVEL: 1   TEXT REFERENCE: 18-6
ANSWER: T

_____ The catalytic path of a chemical reaction has a lower
activation energy than the regular path.

10) TYPE: T   LEVEL: 1   TEXT REFERENCE: 18-6
ANSWER: F

_____ The activated complex in a reaction is the same whether or not
a catalyst is added.

11) TYPE: T   LEVEL: 1   TEXT REFERENCE: 18-7
ANSWER: T

_____ In the equation, rate = k[A]^x[B]^y, [A] and [B] represent the
molar concentrations of the reactants.

12) TYPE: T   LEVEL: 1   TEXT REFERENCE: 18-7
ANSWER: T

_____ In the equation, rate = k[A]^x[B]^y, the letter k is a
proportionality constant.

13) TYPE: T   LEVEL: 1   TEXT REFERENCE: 18-8
ANSWER: F

_____ The reaction mechanism is the slowest reaction in a sequence of
reactions.

14) TYPE: O   LEVEL: 2   TEXT REFERENCE: 18-1
ANSWER: collision

How the interactions between molecules affect reaction rates is
explained by the _____ theory.

15) TYPE: O   LEVEL: 1   TEXT REFERENCE: 18-1
ANSWER: slower

Lithium reacts _____ than potassium at room temperature
when pieces of each element are equal in size, shape, and purity.

16) TYPE: 0   LEVEL: 1   TEXT REFERENCE: 18-1
ANSWER: time

The reaction rate can be expressed as the change in concentration of
a reactant divided by the change in _____.

17) TYPE: 0   LEVEL: 1   TEXT REFERENCE: 18-2
ANSWER: collisions

Increasing the number of reacting particles increases the chances for
effective _____.

18) TYPE: 0   LEVEL: 1   TEXT REFERENCE: 18-2
ANSWER: increased

The rate of a chemical reaction is increased as the concentration of
the reactants is _____.

19) TYPE: 0   LEVEL: 2   TEXT REFERENCE: 18-3
ANSWER: slower

A 10 kg block of magnesium will react with 10 mL of HCl
_____ than will two 5-kg blocks of magnesium.

20) TYPE: 0   LEVEL: 2   TEXT REFERENCE: 18-4
ANSWER: slower

A reaction at 0° C will proceed _____ than will the same
reaction at 10° C.

21) TYPE: 0   LEVEL: 1   TEXT REFERENCE: 18-5
ANSWER: complex

The "molecule" at the top of the energy barrier is called an
activated _____.

22) TYPE: 0   LEVEL: 1   TEXT REFERENCE: 18-5
ANSWER: activation

The energy barrier shows the _____ energy, which is
symbolized by the letter E.

23) TYPE: 0   LEVEL: 1   TEXT REFERENCE: 18-6
ANSWER: catalyst

A _____ is a substance that increases the rate of a
chemical reaction without being used up itself.

24) TYPE: O   LEVEL: 1   TEXT REFERENCE: 18-6
ANSWER: lowers

The use of a contact catalyst _____ the activation energy by
orienting the colliding particles in a more efficient arrangement.

25) TYPE: O   LEVEL: 1   TEXT REFERENCE: 18-6
ANSWER: inhibitor

A reaction may be prevented from occurring by the use of a(n)
_____.

26) TYPE: O   LEVEL: 1   TEXT REFERENCE: 18-7
ANSWER: rate

The proportionality constant, k, is called the _____
constant.

27) TYPE: O   LEVEL: 1   TEXT REFERENCE: 18-7
ANSWER: reactants

At a fixed temperature, the rate of a reaction depends on the
concentrations of the _____.

28) TYPE: O   LEVEL: 1   TEXT REFERENCE: 18-8
ANSWER: mechanism

The sequence of chemical reactions in a complete reaction is called
the reaction _____.

29) TYPE: O   LEVEL: 1   TEXT REFERENCE: 18-8
ANSWER: rate-determing

The slowest reaction in a sequence of reactions is called the
_____ step.

30) TYPE: M   LEVEL: 1   TEXT REFERENCE: 18-1
ANSWER: C

The reaction rate can be expressed as the:

A. total mass of reactants.
B. concentration of reactants.
C. change in concentration of reactants over time.
D. total amount of products.

31) TYPE: M   LEVEL: 2   TEXT REFERENCE: 18-1
ANSWER: D

The rate of a reaction is affected by:

A. temperature.
B. the presence of a catalyst.
C. concentrations of the reactants.
D. all of the above.

32) TYPE: M   LEVEL: 2   TEXT REFERENCE: 18-1
ANSWER: D

The activity of each element is determined by its:

A. ionization energy.   C. electronegativity.
B. atomic radius.   D. all of the above.

33) TYPE: M   LEVEL: 1   TEXT REFERENCE: 18-2
ANSWER: B

In a chemical reaction, if the number of collisons between particles increases, the:

A. reaction rate will decrease.
B. reaction rate will increase.
C. reaction rate will not be increased or decreased.
D. concentration of the reactants will increase.

34) TYPE: M   LEVEL: 2   TEXT REFERENCE: 18-2
ANSWER: A

In the following reaction, if the number of moles of oxygen is increased to two moles, the:
$$2NO(g) + O_2(g) \rightarrow 2NO_2(g) + energy$$

A. reaction speeds up.   C. temperature increases.
B. reaction slows down.   D. temperature decreases.

35) TYPE: M   LEVEL: 2   TEXT REFERENCE: 18-3
ANSWER: D

A chemical reaction taking place on the surface of a block of sodium will not occur faster if the:

A. size of the block doubles.
B. block is cut in half.
C. surface area is increased.
D. amount of sodium is decreased.

36) TYPE: M   LEVEL: 2   TEXT REFERENCE: 18-3
ANSWER: C

Which of the following will burn slowest?

A. a sheet of paper
B. a sheet of paper torn into small pieces
C. a sheet of paper crumpled into a tight ball
D. all of the above will burn at the same rate

37) TYPE: M   LEVEL: 1   TEXT REFERENCE: 18-4
ANSWER: D

In order for a chemical reaction to occur, what conditions must be met?

A. Collisions between atoms cause a rearrangement of atoms.
B. Reacting molecules have energies that together total at least the threshold energy.
C. High energy collisons occur.
D. Both B and C.

38) TYPE: M   LEVEL: 1   TEXT REFERENCE: 18-4
ANSWER: B

The average kinetic energy of gas molecules increases if the :

A. temperature decreases.   C. pressure decreases.
B. temperature increases.   D. reaction rate decreases.

39) TYPE: M   LEVEL: 1   TEXT REFERENCE: 18-5
ANSWER: C

The activated complex has more potential energy than:

A. the reactants.
B. the products.
C. both the reactants and the products.
D. neither the reactants nor the products.

40) TYPE: M   LEVEL: 2   TEXT REFERENCE: 18-5
ANSWER: D

An increase in temperature of ten degrees Celsius in a system will not:

A. increase the average energy.
B. increase the number of particle collisions.
C. increase the reaction rate.
D. increase the activation energy.

41) TYPE: M   LEVEL: 1   TEXT REFERENCE: 18-6
ANSWER: B

If both a catalyst and an inhibitor are used in a chemical reaction,
the reaction may:

A. proceed twice as fast.
B. not occur.
C. proceed as if there was no inhibitor.
D. proceed as if there was no catalyst.

42) TYPE: M   LEVEL: 1   TEXT REFERENCE: 18-6
ANSWER: B

A catalyst speeds up a reaction by providing a:

A. low-energy pathway from products to reactants.
B. low-energy pathway from reactants to products.
C. high-energy pathway from reactants to products.
D. way to overcome the inhibitor.

43) TYPE: M   LEVEL: 1   TEXT REFERENCE: 18-7
ANSWER: D

In the rate equation that follows for a general reaction, which values
must be determined experimentally?
$$k = [A]^x[B]^y$$

A. k, a, and b   C. a and b
B. x and y   D. k, x, and y

44) TYPE: M   LEVEL: 2   TEXT REFERENCE: 18-8
ANSWER: A

In the following series of reactions, which is the rate-determining
step?

$$1.\ HCl(g) + O_2(g) \rightarrow HOOCl(g) \quad (slow)$$
$$2.\ HOOCl(g) + HCl(g) \rightarrow 2HOCl(g) \quad (fast)$$
$$3.\ HOCl(g) + HCl(g) \rightarrow H_2O(g) + Cl_2(g) \quad (fast)$$

A. 1   C. 3
B. 2   D. none of them

45) TYPE: M   LEVEL: 2   TEXT REFERENCE: 18-8
ANSWER: C

In a reaction that takes place in three steps, if the first and third
steps occur more quickly than the second step, the second step is
called the:

A. reaction mechanism.
B. catalyst.
C. rate-determining step.
D. reaction-determining step.

46) TYPE: M   LEVEL: 4   TEXT REFERENCE: LA
ANSWER: B

Which of the following reactions has the fastest reaction rate?

A. the reaction of 10 mL 0.5M HCl with a 5-g block of Mg
B. the reaction of 10 mL 0.5M HCl with a 5-g ribbon of Mg
C. the reaction of 5 mL 0.1M HCl with a 10-g block of Mg
D. A and B have the same reaction rates

47) TYPE: M   LEVEL: 4   TEXT REFERENCE: LA
ANSWER: C

If the reaction rate of a chemical reaction increases, it is possible
that:

A. the concentration of the reactants has decreased.
B. the temperature has decreased.
C. a catalyst has been used.
D. both A and B.

48) TYPE: M   LEVEL: 4   TEXT REFERENCE: LA
ANSWER: A

In a reaction between a 2-g block of Mg and 10 mL of 0.5M HCl, if you
double the amount of HCl used, the reaction rate will:

A. speed up.   C. stay the same.
B. slow down.   D. cannot tell.

49) TYPE: M   LEVEL: 4   TEXT REFERENCE: LA
ANSWER: A

In a reaction between Mg and HCl, using which form of magnesium will
cause the reaction to proceed the fastest?

A. slivers.
B. rolls.
C. strips.
D. the reaction rate will be the same for any shape.

50) TYPE: M   LEVEL: 4   TEXT REFERENCE: LA
ANSWER: C

In the reaction between magnesium metal and hydrochloric acid, what
was produced?

A. magnesium chloride   C. both A and B
B. hydrogen gas   D. none of the above

51) TYPE: M   LEVEL: 4   TEXT REFERENCE: LB
ANSWER: B

What type of substance may be used to slow down a reaction?

A. a catalyst   C. both A and B
B. an inhibitor   D. none of the above

52) TYPE: O   LEVEL: 4   TEXT REFERENCE: LB
ANSWER: A

In the "Iodine Clock" experiment, starch is used to detect the
presence of:

A. iodine.   C. potassium.
B. copper sulfate.   D. ammonium ions.

53) TYPE: M   LEVEL: 4   TEXT REFERENCE: LB
ANSWER: A

In the "Iodine Clock" reaction, increasing the concentration of
solution A would:

A. increase the reaction rate.
B. decrease the reaction rate.
C. not affect the reaction rate.
D. stop the reaction.

54) TYPE: M   LEVEL: 4   TEXT REFERENCE: LB
ANSWER: A

In the "Iodine Clock" reaction, the addition of 0.01M copper sulfate
solution:

A. increased the reaction rate.
B. decreased the reaction rate.
C. decreased the amount of product.
D. did not affect the reaction.

Chapter 19   REACTION EQUILIBRIUM

1) TYPE: T   LEVEL: 2   TEXT REFERENCE: 19-1
ANSWER: T

_____   In a reversible reaction, the formation of products and the
reformation of reactants occur at the same time.

2) TYPE: T   LEVEL: 2   TEXT REFERENCE: 19-2
ANSWER: F

_____   Both reversible reactions and completion reactions can reach
equilibrium.

3) TYPE: T   LEVEL: 1   TEXT REFERENCE: 19-2
ANSWER: F

_____   At equilibrium, the concentrations of the products is always
equal to the concentration of the reactants.

4) TYPE: T   LEVEL: 2   TEXT REFERENCE: 19-3
ANSWER: F

_____   Increasing the temperature of an equilibrium system favors the
exothermic reaction until a new equilibrium state is reached.

5) TYPE: T   LEVEL: 2   TEXT REFERENCE: 19-3
ANSWER: T

_____   For a system at equilibrium, an increase in pressure favors the
production of fewer molecules.

6) TYPE: T   LEVEL: 2   TEXT REFERENCE: 19-4
ANSWER: F

_____   In a reversible reaction at equilibrium, increasing the
concentration of a product favors the forward reaction until a
new equilibrium is reached.

7) TYPE: T   LEVEL: 1   TEXT REFERENCE: 19-5
ANSWER: T

_____   A catalyst has no net effect on an equilibrium system.

8) TYPE: T   LEVEL: 2   TEXT REFERENCE: 19-6
ANSWER: T

_____   Le Chatelier's principle implies that if a system in
        equilibrium is subjected to a change, a shift in the original
        equilibrium will occur.

9) TYPE: T   LEVEL: 3   TEXT REFERENCE: 19-7
ANSWER: T

_____   The Haber process makes use of an equilibrium system to
        manufacture ammonia.

10) TYPE: T   LEVEL: 1   TEXT REFERENCE: 19-8
ANSWER: T

_____   The equilibrium constant shows the ratio of product
        concentration terms to reactant concentration terms.

11) TYPE: T   LEVEL: 2   TEXT REFERENCE: 19-8
ANSWER: F

_____   The equilibrium constant is zero when concentration of both
        reactants and products is low.

12) TYPE: T   LEVEL: 2   TEXT REFERENCE: 19-9
ANSWER: T

_____   Raising the temperature of an exothermic reaction reduces the
        equilibrium constant.

13) TYPE: T   LEVEL: 1   TEXT REFERENCE: 19-10
ANSWER: T

_____   The concentration of a solid is constant.

14) TYPE: T   LEVEL: 1   TEXT REFERENCE: 19-11
ANSWER: T

_____   Le Chatelier's principle can be used to describe how an
        equilibrium system responds to changes in concentration of ions
        in an aqueous solution.

15) TYPE: O   LEVEL: 1   TEXT REFERENCE: 19-1
ANSWER: reversible

A reaction in which the product may react to form the reactant is
called a(n) _____ reaction.

16) TYPE: 0   LEVEL: 1   TEXT REFERENCE: 19-1
ANSWER: chemical equilibrium

When opposing reactions occur at the same rate, and no observable changes are taking place, _____ has been reached.

17) TYPE: 0   LEVEL: 1   TEXT REFERENCE: 19-2
ANSWER: opposite

One condition for equilibrium is that _____ reactions are occurring at the same rate.

18) TYPE: 0   LEVEL: 1   TEXT REFERENCE: 19-2
ANSWER: increases

Raising the temperature of a system _____ the rate of reaction.

19) TYPE: 0   LEVEL: 1   TEXT REFERENCE: 19-3
ANSWER: smallest

Increasing the pressure of a system favors the reaction that produces the _____ number of particles.

20) TYPE: 0   LEVEL: 1   TEXT REFERENCE: 19-5
ANSWER: energy barrier

A catalyst lowers the _____ for a reaction.

21) TYPE: 0   LEVEL: 2   TEXT REFERENCE: 19-6
ANSWER: increase

If the equilibrium for a reaction is shifted to the right, the concentration of the products will _____.

22) TYPE: 0   LEVEL: 3   TEXT REFERENCE: 19-7
ANSWER: high

The Haber process utilizes high pressure and _____ temperatures in conjunction with a catalyst to produce the maximum yield of ammonia.

23) TYPE: 0   LEVEL: 1   TEXT REFERENCE: 19-8
ANSWER: K_{eq}

The equilibrium constant is represented by the symbol _____.

24) **TYPE:** O   **LEVEL:** 1   **TEXT REFERENCE:** 19-8
ANSWER: products

The concentration of _____ is in the numerator of the equilibrium constant.

25) **TYPE:** O   **LEVEL:** 1   **TEXT REFERENCE:** 19-8
ANSWER: reactants

A small equilibrium constant indicates that the _____ are favored at equilibrium.

26) **TYPE:** O   **LEVEL:** 2   **TEXT REFERENCE:** 19-9
ANSWER: increases

In an exothermic reaction, if the temperature increases, the amount of reactants increases and the value of the denominator in the equilibrium constant _____.

27) **TYPE:** O   **LEVEL:** 1   **TEXT REFERENCE:** 19-11
ANSWER: spectator

The addition of _____ ions has no effect on an equilibrium system between ions in solution.

28) **TYPE:** M   **LEVEL:** 2   **TEXT REFERENCE:** 19-1
ANSWER: D

Which of the following is a properly balanced equation representing a reversible reaction?

A. P_2O_4 + energy $\rightarrow$ $2PO_2(g)$
B. $2PO_2(g)$ $\rightarrow$ P_2O_4 + energy
C. $PO_2(g)$ $\rightleftharpoons$ P_2O_4 + energy
D. $2PO_2(g)$ $\rightleftharpoons$ P_2O_4 + energy

29) **TYPE:** M   **LEVEL:** 1   **TEXT REFERENCE:** 19-2
ANSWER: D

In an equilibrium system the rate of the reverse reaction equals the rate of the:

A. completion reaction.
B. decomposition reaction.
C. equilibrium state.
D. forward reaction.

Chapter 19   REACTION EQUILIBRIUM

30) TYPE: M   LEVEL: 2   TEXT REFERENCE: 19-2
ANSWER: B

The reverse reaction of a given equilibrium reaction is favored by an increase in temperature. If the reaction involves red reactants and colorless products how will the appearance of the system change when heated?

A. Eventually the whole system will become lighter.
B. Eventually the whole system will become darker.
C. The reactants will become darker.
D. The products will become lighter.

31) TYPE: M   LEVEL: 2   TEXT REFERENCE: 19-3
ANSWER: D

An increase in pressure of an equilibrium system will favor the:

A. forward reaction.
B. reverse reaction.
C. reaction which produces the most moles per unit volume.
D. reaction which produces the fewest moles per unit volume.

32) TYPE: M   LEVEL: 1   TEXT REFERENCE: 19-3
ANSWER: C

In the following reversible reaction, an increase in pressure will favor which reaction?
$$2HCl(g) \rightleftharpoons H_2(g) + Cl_2(g)$$

A. the forward reaction
B. the reverse reaction
C. neither the forward nor the reverse reaction
D. cannot tell

33) TYPE: M   LEVEL: 2   TEXT REFERENCE: 19-3
ANSWER: B

In the following reversible reaction, a decrease in pressure will favor which reaction?
$$2PO_2(g) \rightleftharpoons P_2O_4(g) + energy$$

A. the forward reaction
B. the reverse reaction
C. neither the forward nor the reverse reaction
D. cannot tell

34) TYPE: M   LEVEL: 2   TEXT REFERENCE: 19-4
ANSWER: C

In the following reaction, if the concentration of HCl is increased,
the concentration of:

$$2HCl(g) \rightleftharpoons H_2(g) + Cl_2(g)$$

A. H_2 will increase
B. Cl_2 will increase
C. both H_2 and Cl_2 will increase
D. both H_2 and Cl_2 will decrease

35) TYPE: M   LEVEL: 1   TEXT REFERENCE: 19-5
ANSWER: C

In an equilibrium system, a catalyst affects the:

A. concentration of the reactants.
B. concentration of the products.
C. time required to reach equilibrium.
D. both A and B.

36) TYPE: M   LEVEL: 2   TEXT REFERENCE: 19-6
ANSWER: B

If the equilibrium for a reaction is shifted to the left, the:

A. concentration of the products will increase.
B. concentration of the reactants will increase.
C. synthesis reaction will be favored.
D. concentrations cannot be determined.

37) TYPE: M   LEVEL: 2   TEXT REFERENCE: 19-8
ANSWER: D

The equilibrium constant $K_{eq} = \dfrac{[HCl]^2}{[H_2][Cl_2]}$

represents the system:

A. $H_2 + Cl_2 \rightleftharpoons HCl$.
B. $H_2 + Cl_2 \rightleftharpoons [HCl]^2$.
C. $2H + 2Cl \rightleftharpoons 2HCl$.
D. $H_2 + Cl_2 \rightleftharpoons 2HCl$.

38) TYPE: M   LEVEL: 2   TEXT REFERENCE: 19-8
ANSWER: A

The equilibrium constant "626 at 200 degrees Celsius" indicates that
the reaction favors the:

A. products.
B. reactants.
C. neither the products nor the reactants.
D. products and the reactants equally.

39) TYPE: M   LEVEL: 2   TEXT REFERENCE: 19-8
ANSWER: C

The equilibrium system represented by the following expression is:
$$K_{eq} = \frac{[SO_3]^2}{[SO_2]^2[O_2]}$$

A. $SO_2(g) + O_2 \rightleftharpoons SO_3(g)$.
B. $SO_2(g) \rightleftharpoons O_2(g) + SO_3(g)$
C. $2SO_2(g) + O_2(g) \rightleftharpoons 2SO_3(g)$.
D. $4SO(g) + 2O(g) \rightleftharpoons 6SO(g)$.

40) TYPE: M   LEVEL: 1   TEXT REFERENCE: 19-9
ANSWER: B

Raising the temperature of a forward, endothermic reaction in an
equilibrium system:

A. reduces the K_{eq}.
B. increases the K_{eq}.
C. does not affect the K_{eq}.
D. may either increase or decrease the K_{eq}.

41) TYPE: M   LEVEL: 2   TEXT REFERENCE: 19-9
ANSWER: B

If the temperature of a forward, exothermic reaction of an
equilibrium system is lowered, the value of the denominator in the
expression for the equilibrium constant will:

A. increase.
B. decrease.
C. remain the same.
D. equal the value of the numerator.

42) TYPE: M   LEVEL: 2   TEXT REFERENCE: 19-10
ANSWER: D

In an equilibrium system involving solids and gases, an increase in
the amount of solid reactant will:

A. increase the concentration of the gas product.
B. decrease the concentration of the gas product.
C. increase the concentration of all products.
D. not affect the concentration of the gas product.

43) TYPE: M   LEVEL: 1   TEXT REFERENCE: 19-10
ANSWER: B

The concentration for solids and pure liquids are omitted from an
equilibrium expression because they are:

A. unimportant.
B. constant.
C. close to zero.
D. equal.

44) TYPE: M   LEVEL: 2   TEXT REFERENCE: 19-10
ANSWER: D

What is the equilibrium expression for the following reaction?
$$H_2S(g) \rightleftharpoons S(l) + H_2(g)$$

A. $K_{eq} = [S]$
B. $K_{eq} = [H_2]$
C. $K_{eq} = [H_2S]$
D. none of the above

45) TYPE: M   LEVEL: 2   TEXT REFERENCE: LA
ANSWER: A

In the following equilibrium system, which reaction is favored?
$$Fe^{3+}(aq) + SCN^-(aq) \rightleftharpoons FeSCN^{2+}(aq)$$

A. forward   C. reverse
B. neither   D. cannot tell

46) TYPE: M   LEVEL: 4   TEXT REFERENCE: LA
ANSWER: C

In the following equilibrium system, if there is an increase in
temperature, which reaction will be favored?
$$Co(H_2O)_6^{2+}(aq) + 2Cl^-(aq) \rightleftharpoons$$
$$Co(H_2O)_4Cl_2(aq) + 2H_2O(l)$$

A. exothermic   C. forward
B. reverse   D. neither

47) TYPE: M   LEVEL: 4   TEXT REFERENCE: LA
ANSWER: C

The indicator thymal blue changes color in the presence of:

A. Fe^{3+} ions.   C. hydrogen ions.
B. cobalt ions.   D. a catalyst.

48) TYPE: M   LEVEL: 4   TEXT REFERENCE: LA
ANSWER: D

Macroscopic evidence of a stress placed on an equilibrium system
would include:

A. formation of a precipitate.
B. variation in color.
C. increased ion production.
D. both A and B.

Chapter 20 ACID-BASE REACTIONS

1) TYPE: T   LEVEL: 1   TEXT REFERENCE: 20-1
ANSWER: T

_____ Both acids and bases conduct electricity.

2) TYPE: T   LEVEL: 2   TEXT REFERENCE: 20-2
ANSWER: T

_____ Water is an amphiprotic substance.

3) TYPE: T   LEVEL: 1   TEXT REFERENCE: 20-2
ANSWER: F

_____ Acids can accept a proton while bases can donate a proton.

4) TYPE: T   LEVEL: 1   TEXT REFERENCE: 20-3
ANSWER: F

_____ Conjugate acid-base pairs differ only by an electron.

5) TYPE: T   LEVEL: 2   TEXT REFERENCE: 20-5
ANSWER: T

_____ Sodium hydroxide is commonly used to clean clogged drains.

6) TYPE: T   LEVEL: 1   TEXT REFERENCE: 20-6
ANSWER: T

_____ Both strong acids and stong bases react completely with water.

7) TYPE: T   LEVEL: 2   TEXT REFERENCE: 20-7
ANSWER: F

_____ Ammonia is an acid that reacts completely with water.

8) TYPE: T   LEVEL: 2   TEXT REFERENCE: 20-9
ANSWER: T

_____ In the equation for the reaction of HF with water, the water
       molecule on the reactant side is a base.

9) TYPE: T   LEVEL: 2   TEXT REFERENCE: 20-11
ANSWER: T

_____ An indicator can exist in two forms, each form having a
       distinct color.

10) TYPE: T   LEVEL: 2   TEXT REFERENCE: 20-12
ANSWER: F

_____   The hydronium ion concentration in water is ten times as large
         as the hydronium concentration in a 10M solution of HCl.

11) TYPE: T   LEVEL: 1   TEXT REFERENCE: 20-14
ANSWER: F

_____   The equivalence point is where the proportion of reactants
         equals the proportion of products.

12) TYPE: T   LEVEL: 1   TEXT REFERENCE: 20-15
ANSWER: T

_____   Salts are ionic compounds.

13) TYPE: T   LEVEL: 1   TEXT REFERENCE: 20-17
ANSWER: T

_____   When a basic anhydride and an acidic anhydride combine, they
         form a salt.

14) TYPE: O   LEVEL: 1   TEXT REFERENCE: 20-1
ANSWER: base

One characteristic of a(n) _____ is that it tastes
bitter.

15) TYPE: O   LEVEL: 1   TEXT REFERENCE: 20-2
ANSWER: indicators

Compounds called _____ are used to detect the presence
of H^+.

16) TYPE: O   LEVEL: 1   TEXT REFERENCE: 20-2
ANSWER: neutralization

When moles of protons donated by the acid and moles of protons
accepted by the base are equal, _____ occurs.

17) TYPE: O   LEVEL: 1   TEXT REFERENCE: 20-3
ANSWER: monoprotic

Acids and bases that exchange one proton are called _____.

18) TYPE: O   LEVEL: 1   TEXT REFERENCE: 20-4
ANSWER: binary

Direct combination of a nonmetallic element with hydrogen gas may
result in a(n) _____ acid.

19) TYPE: O   LEVEL: 1   TEXT REFERENCE: 20-4
ANSWER: HF

The formula for hydrofluoric acid is _____.

20) TYPE: O   LEVEL: 1   TEXT REFERENCE: 20-6
ANSWER: weak

An acid that does not react completely with water is called a(n)
_____ acid.

21) TYPE: O   LEVEL: 1   TEXT REFERENCE: 20-7
ANSWER: ammonia

The most common weak base is _____.

22) TYPE: O   LEVEL: 1   TEXT REFERENCE: 20-8
ANSWER: donates

A strong base readily _____ protons.

23) TYPE: O   LEVEL: 1   TEXT REFERENCE: 20-9
ANSWER: K_a

The acid dissociation constant is represented by the symbol
_____.

24) TYPE: O   LEVEL: 1   TEXT REFERENCE: 20-10
ANSWER: 1×10^{-14}

The dissociation, or ion product, constant for water is equal to
_____.

25) TYPE: O   LEVEL: 1   TEXT REFERENCE: 20-11
ANSWER: hydronium

An indicator provides information about the concentration of
_____ ions in a solution.

26) TYPE: 0   LEVEL: 1   TEXT REFERENCE: 20-13
ANSWER: seven

A neutral solution has a pH of _____.

27) TYPE: 0   LEVEL: 1   TEXT REFERENCE: 20-14
ANSWER: titration

A method used to find the concentration of a strong acid solution by
adding a strong base of known concentration to the solution is called
_____.

28) TYPE: 0   LEVEL: 1   TEXT REFERENCE: 20-17
ANSWER: anhydride

An oxygen-containing compound that dissolves in water producing an
acid is called an acidic _____.

29) TYPE: 0   LEVEL: 1   TEXT REFERENCE: 20-19
ANSWER: buffer

A solution that can remain at a near constant pH even when small
amounts of an acid or base is added to it is called a(n)
_____.

30) TYPE: M   LEVEL: 1   TEXT REFERENCE: 20-1
ANSWER: C

Which of the folllowing is not a characteristic of an acid?

A. tastes sour.
B. causes certain dyes to change color.
C. feels slippery.
D. releases hydrogen when it reacts with certain metals.

31) TYPE: M   LEVEL: 2   TEXT REFERENCE: 20-1
ANSWER: D

A solution that does not conduct electricity:

A. is a base.   C. contains ions.
B. is an acid.   D. does not contain ions.

32) TYPE: M   LEVEL: 1   TEXT REFERENCE: 20-2
ANSWER: B

A hydrated proton is a:

A. hydration ion.   C. hydronium proton.
B. hydronium ion.   D. hydrogen ion.

184

33) TYPE: M   LEVEL: 1   TEXT REFERENCE: 20-2
ANSWER: C

One characteristic of a base as defined by Bronsted and Lowry is:

A. a bitter taste.
B. the ability to conduct an electric current.
C. the ability to accept a proton in a reaction.
D. the inability to conduct an electric current.

34) TYPE: M   LEVEL: 2   TEXT REFERENCE: 20-3
ANSWER: D

Which of the following is not a conjugate acid-base pair?

A. NH_3 and NH_4^+ C. PH_3 and PH_4^+
B. water and OH^- D. H_2O and $2H_2O$

35) TYPE: M   LEVEL: 1   TEXT REFERENCE: 20-3
ANSWER: C

If a substance is capable of donating more than one proton, it is
called a(n):

A. acid.   C. polyprotic acid.
B. monoprotic acid.   D. polyprotic base.

36) TYPE: M   LEVEL: 1   TEXT REFERENCE: 20-4
ANSWER: B

One characteristic of nitric acid is not:

A. a suffocating odor.
B. a reddish color.
C. that it leaves a yellow stain on the skin.
D. a high solubility in water.

37) TYPE: M   LEVEL: 1   TEXT REFERENCE: 20-4
ANSWER: C

Chloric acid is a(n):

A. binary acid.   C. ternary acid.
B. tertiary acid.   D. Ostwald acid.

38) TYPE: M   LEVEL: 2   TEXT REFERENCE: 20-5
ANSWER: A

Liquid Drano working to unclog hair from a drain is:

A. sodium hydroxide reacting with protein.
B. sodium hydroxide reacting with fats.
C. aluminum flakes reacting with protein.
D. aluminum flakes reacting with sodium hydroxide.

39) TYPE: M   LEVEL: 1   TEXT REFERENCE: 20-6
ANSWER: B

The strength of an acid depends on the number of:

A. hydrogen ions produced per mole of acid.
B. hydronium ions produced per mole of acid.
C. hydronium ions produced per mole of water.
D. hydronium atoms produced per unit of solvent.

40) TYPE: M   LEVEL: 2   TEXT REFERENCE: 20-7
ANSWER: D

One example of weak base is:

A. HBr.   C. H_2SO_4.
B. KOH.   D. ammonia.

41) TYPE: M   LEVEL: 1   TEXT REFERENCE: 20-7
ANSWER: C

Strong bases are formed from water and:

A. heavy metals.
B. group I metals.
C. group I metals and some group II metals.
D. group II metals.

42) TYPE: M   LEVEL: 2   TEXT REFERENCE: 20-8
ANSWER: D

The base formula for a chloride ion is:

A. H + Cl.   C. HCl.
B. H^+ + Cl.   D. Cl^-.

43) TYPE: M   LEVEL: 2   TEXT REFERENCE: 20-8
ANSWER: A

Which of the following completes the equation
$$PO_4^{3-} + HCl \rightarrow ?$$

A. $HPO_4^{2-} + Cl^-$ C. $H^+ + PO_4^{2-} + Cl^-$
B. $HPO_4^{3-} + Cl^-$ D. $H^+ + Cl^-$

44) TYPE: M   LEVEL: 1   TEXT REFERENCE: 20-10
ANSWER: C

The symbol K_w represents:

A. $[H_2O^+][OH^-]$.   C. $[H_3O^+][OH^-]$.
B. $[H_2O][OH^-]$.   D. $[H_2O][OH]$.

45) TYPE: M   LEVEL: 2   TEXT REFERENCE: 20-11
ANSWER: A

If an indicator carries a negative charge as a product, the indicator
is a(n):

A. weak acid.   C. strong acid.
B. weak base.   D. strong base.

46) TYPE: M   LEVEL: 1   TEXT REFERENCE: 20-12
ANSWER: C

The hydronium ion concentration for different solutions:

A. is the same for every solution.
B. is always very low.
C. can vary a great deal.
D. is between 1M and 10M.

47) TYPE: M   LEVEL: 1   TEXT REFERENCE: 20-13
ANSWER: A

The value equal to $-log[H_3O^+]$ is represented by the symbol:

A. pH.   C. pOH.
B. -pH.   D. -pOH.

48) TYPE: M   LEVEL: 2   TEXT REFERENCE: 20-13
ANSWER: D

Lemon juice has a pH higher than:

A. seawater.   C. 5.
B. human blood.   D. 1M HCl.

49) TYPE: M   LEVEL: 2   TEXT REFERENCE: 20-14
ANSWER: B

What is the concentration of acid in rainwater when 100 mL are
titrated against 32.16 mL of 0.002 01M NaOH?

A. 6.46×10^4 C. 6.46×10^{-5}
B. 6.46×10^{-4} D. 3.22×10^{-5}

50) TYPE: M   LEVEL: 1   TEXT REFERENCE: 20-15
ANSWER: D

Neutralization reactions between an acid and a base produce a(n):

A. buffer.   C. anhydride.
B. aspirin.   D. salt.

51) TYPE: M   LEVEL: 2   TEXT REFERENCE: 20-16
ANSWER: A

Salts of a strong base and a weak acid will produce a solution that
is:

A. slightly basic.   C. neutral.
B. slightly acidic.   D. strongly basic.

52) TYPE: M   LEVEL: 2   TEXT REFERENCE: 20-16
ANSWER: C

Salts of a strong base and a strong acid will produce a solution
whose pH is:

A. 0.   C. 7.
B. 1.   D. 10.

53) TYPE: M   LEVEL: 1   TEXT REFERENCE: 20-17
ANSWER: D

What does the word anhydride mean?

A. water-producing   C. without salt
B. full of water   D. without water

54) TYPE: M   LEVEL: 2   TEXT REFERENCE: 20-17
ANSWER: C

What is the anhydride in the following equation?
$$Mg(OH)_2 \rightarrow MgO + H_2O$$

A. Mg   C. MgO
B. H_2O D. $Mg(OH)_2$

55) TYPE: M   LEVEL: 3   TEXT REFERENCE: 20-18
ANSWER: A

The reddish-brown color of smog in the atmosphere is due to the
presence of:

A. NO_2.   C. HNO_3.
B. HNO_2.   D. SO_2.

56) TYPE: M   LEVEL: 2   TEXT REFERENCE: 20-19
ANSWER: C

Which of the following contains a buffer?

A. pure water   C. human blood
B. HCl   D. sodium hydroxide

57) TYPE: M   LEVEL: 4   TEXT REFERENCE: LA
ANSWER: C

What would you use as a standard when titrating against a weak
carbonic acid solution?

A. a weak acid   C. a weak base
B. a strong acid   D. a strong base

58) TYPE: M   LEVEL: 4   TEXT REFERENCE: LA
ANSWER: A

The most effective indicator to use when doing a titration is an
indicator whose overall color:

A. darkens.   C. stays the same.
B. lightens.   D. is unimportant.

59) TYPE: M   LEVEL: 4   TEXT REFERENCE: LA
ANSWER: B

If 10 mL of HCl are added to ammonia to reach the equivalence point,
how much H_2SO_4 of the same molar concentration would be added to
the same amount of ammonia to reach the equivalence point?

A. 10 mL   C. 20 mL
B. 5 mL   D. none of the above

60) TYPE: M   LEVEL: 4   TEXT REFERENCE: LB
ANSWER: C

The gas that is released when acid solutions react with magnesium is:

A. oxygen.   C. hydrogen.
B. chlorine.   D. NO_2.

61) TYPE: M   LEVEL: 4   TEXT REFERENCE: LB
ANSWER: B

The addition of lime to an acidic soil filtrate will:

A. increase the acidity.
B. decrease the acidity.
C. not affect the pH.
D. produce hydrogen gas.

62) TYPE: M   LEVEL: 4   TEXT REFERENCE: LB
ANSWER: A

What is the balanced equation for the reaction between nitrogen
dioxide and water vapor?

A. $3NO_2(g) + H_2O(g) \rightarrow 2HNO_3(l) + NO(g)$
B. $3NO_2(g) + H_2O(g) \rightarrow HNO_3(l) + NO(g)$
C. $NO_2(g) + H_2O(g) \rightarrow HNO_3(l) + NO(g)$
D. $NO_2(g) + 2H_2O(g) \rightarrow HNO_3(l) + 2NO(g)$

63) TYPE: M   LEVEL: 4   TEXT REFERENCE: LB
ANSWER: D

Which of the following produces acid rain?

A. SO_2 C. SO_3
B. NO_2 D. all of the above

64) TYPE: M   LEVEL: 4   TEXT REFERENCE: LB
ANSWER: B

Soils are naturally protected against acid rain if they are rich in:

A. nitrates.
B. CaO.

C. H_2SO_4.
D. all of the above.

1) TYPE: T   LEVEL: 1   TEXT REFERENCE: 21-1
ANSWER: F

_____ Reduction reactions represent a loss of electrons, while
oxidation reactions represent a gain of electrons.

2) TYPE: T   LEVEL: 1   TEXT REFERENCE: 21-1
ANSWER: F

_____ In a redox reaction, the substance that is oxidized is known as
the oxidizing agent.

3) TYPE: T   LEVEL: 1   TEXT REFERENCE: 21-2
ANSWER: T

_____ An assumption made when determining the oxidation number of an
atom is that all bonding electrons belong to the atom with the
higher electronegativity.

4) TYPE: T   LEVEL: 1   TEXT REFERENCE: 21-2
ANSWER: F

_____ It is necessary to know the state of an element when determining
its oxidation number.

5) TYPE: T   LEVEL: 1   TEXT REFERENCE: 21-4
ANSWER: T

_____ An example of an electrochemical cell is the battery that powers
a flashlight.

6) TYPE: T   LEVEL: 2   TEXT REFERENCE: 21-4
ANSWER: T

_____ A metal that is a strong reducing agent will most likely be
found in nature in its oxidized state.

7) TYPE: T   LEVEL: 2   TEXT REFERENCE: 21-5
ANSWER: T

_____ The half-cell potential describes the tendency of an atom to
gain or lose electrons.

8) TYPE: T   LEVEL: 1   TEXT REFERENCE: 21-5
ANSWER: T

_____   An ampere is a unit that describes the rate of flow of
        electricity.

9) TYPE: T   LEVEL: 1   TEXT REFERENCE: 21-6
ANSWER: F

_____   At equilibrium in a redox reaction, the concentrations of the
        solutions are 1M.

10) TYPE: T   LEVEL: 1   TEXT REFERENCE: 21-6
ANSWER: T

_____   At equilibrium in a redox reaction, the voltage is zero.

11) TYPE: T   LEVEL: 1   TEXT REFERENCE: 21-7
ANSWER: T

_____   An alkaline manganese cell is more efficient than a Leclanche
        cell.

12) TYPE: T   LEVEL: 1   TEXT REFERENCE: 21-7
ANSWER: F

_____   Most car batteries are very powerful lithium-sulfur dioxide
        batteries.

13) TYPE: T   LEVEL: 1   TEXT REFERENCE: 21-9
ANSWER: F

_____   An external source of energy may be used to cause a spontaneous
        redox reaction.

14) TYPE: T   LEVEL: 1   TEXT REFERENCE: 21-9
ANSWER: T

_____   The amount of energy needed to recycle aluminum is very small
        compared to the amount of energy needed to extract aluminum from
        its ore.

15) TYPE: T   LEVEL: 3   TEXT REFERENCE: 21-10
ANSWER: T

_____   Metal will corrode faster if it is in direct contact with
        another piece of metal.

16) TYPE: 0   LEVEL: 1   TEXT REFERENCE: 21-1
ANSWER: redox

Two half-reactions are required to completely describe any
_____ reaction.

17) TYPE: 0   LEVEL: 1   TEXT REFERENCE: 21-1
ANSWER: oxidizing

In a redox reaction, the substance that is reduced is the
_____ agent.

18) TYPE: 0   LEVEL: 2   TEXT REFERENCE: 21-2
ANSWER: electronegativity

The attraction an atom has for shared pairs of electrons in a
covalent bond with another atom is called its _____.

19) TYPE: 0   LEVEL: 1   TEXT REFERENCE: 21-2
ANSWER: 2-

The oxidation number for oxygen, except in peroxides, is
_____.

20) TYPE: 0   LEVEL: 2   TEXT REFERENCE: 21-3
ANSWER: $2e^-$, Zn

The complete half-reaction for the reduction of the zinc ion to
zinc metal is:
$$Zn^{2+} + \underline{\hspace{3cm}} \rightarrow \underline{\hspace{3cm}} .$$

21) TYPE: 0   LEVEL: 1   TEXT REFERENCE: 21-4
ANSWER: cell

An electrochemical _____ is a system in which a
spontaneous redox reaction can produce useful work.

22) TYPE: 0   LEVEL: 1   TEXT REFERENCE: 21-4
ANSWER: anode

In an electrochemical cell, the site of oxidation is called the
_____.

23) TYPE: 0   LEVEL: 1   TEXT REFERENCE: 21-5
ANSWER: coulomb

1.04×10^{-5} mole of electrons is equal to one _____.

24) TYPE: 0   LEVEL: 1   TEXT REFERENCE: 21-5
ANSWER: potential

The contribution made to the cell voltage by each half-cell reaction
is the half-cell _____.

25) TYPE: 0   LEVEL: 1   TEXT REFERENCE: 21-6
ANSWER: positive

A redox reaction will occur spontaneously if the cell voltage is
_____.

26) TYPE: 0   LEVEL: 1   TEXT REFERENCE: 21-7
ANSWER: dry

A common battery in which the electrolytes are present as a solid or
a paste is known as a(n) _____ cell.

27) TYPE: 0   LEVEL: 1   TEXT REFERENCE: 21-7
ANSWER: more

An alkaline battery yields _____ current than the
Leclanche cell.

28) TYPE: 0   LEVEL: 1   TEXT REFERENCE: 21-9
ANSWER: electrolysis

A method using an external energy supply to separate valuable
substances from aqueous solutions is called _____.

29) TYPE: 0   LEVEL: 1   TEXT REFERENCE: 21-9
ANSWER: negative

A(n) _____ voltage indicates that a reaction is not
spontaneous.

30) TYPE: 0   LEVEL: 3   TEXT REFERENCE: 21-10
ANSWER: rust

The corrosion of iron results in the formation of flakes of
_____.

31) TYPE: 0   LEVEL: 3   TEXT REFERENCE: 21-10
ANSWER: cathodic

Attaching metals that are more easily oxidized as a means of
preserving iron objects is called _____ protection.

32) TYPE: M   LEVEL: 2   TEXT REFERENCE: 21-1
ANSWER: B

Which of the following is a balanced redox reaction?

A. $Ag^2(aq) + B(s) \rightarrow Ag(s) + B^{3+}$
B. $3Ag^{2+} + 2B(s) \rightarrow 3Ag(s) + 2B^{3+}(aq)$
C. $3Ag^{2+} + 2B(s) + 6e^- \rightarrow 3Ag(s) + 2B^{3+}(aq) + 6e^-$
D. $Ag^{2+}(aq) + 3B(s) \rightarrow 2Ag(s) + B^{3+}$

33) TYPE: M   LEVEL: 2   TEXT REFERENCE: 21-1
ANSWER: A

In the following equation, Cd is the:
$$2Au^{3+}(aq) + 3Cd(s) \rightarrow 2Au(s) + 3Cd^{2+}(aq)$$

A. reducing agent.   C. substance that is reduced.
B. oxidizing agent.   D. redox agent.

34) TYPE: M   LEVEL: 2   TEXT REFERENCE: 21-1
ANSWER: B

In the following equation, what substance has been oxidized?
$$2Fe^{3+}(aq) + 6Al(s) \rightarrow 3Fe^{2+}(aq) + 2Al^{3+}(aq)$$

A. Fe^{3+} C. Fe^{2+}
B. Al   D. Al^{3+}

35) TYPE: M   LEVEL: 1   TEXT REFERENCE: 21-2
ANSWER: C

The oxidation number for the alkali metals in compounds is:

A. 0.   C. 1+.
B. 1-.   D. 2+.

36) TYPE: M   LEVEL: 2   TEXT REFERENCE: 21-2
ANSWER: D

What is the oxidation number of sulfur in the sulfite ion SO_4^{2-}?

A. 4+   C. 2+
B. 4-   D. 6+

37) TYPE: M   LEVEL: 2   TEXT REFERENCE: 21-2
ANSWER: A

When NO_3^- is decomposed to form elemental nitrogen, the nitrogen is:

A. reduced.   C. stays the same.
B. oxidized.   D. either reduced or oxidized.

38) TYPE: M   LEVEL: 2   TEXT REFERENCE: 21-3
ANSWER: B

The balanced half-reaction for zinc in the following reaction is:
$$Zn + K^+ + SO_2^- \rightarrow K^+ + SO^{2+} + Zn^{2+}$$

A. $Zn \rightarrow Zn^{2+}$.
B. $Zn \rightarrow Zn^{2+} + 2e^-$.
C. $2Zn \rightarrow Zn^{2+}$.
D. $2Zn \rightarrow Zn^{2+} + 2e^-$.

39) TYPE: M   LEVEL: 2   TEXT REFERENCE: 21-3
ANSWER: B

What is the balanced form of the following equation?
$$Zn + NO_3^- + H^+ \rightarrow Zn^{2+} + NH_4^+ + H_2O$$

A. $Zn + NO_3^- + H^+ \rightarrow Zn^{2+} + NH_4^+ + H_2O$
B. $4Zn + NO_3^- + 10H^+ \rightarrow NH_4^+ + 3H_2O + 4Zn^{2+}$
C. $2Zn + NO_3^- + 6H^+ \rightarrow NH_4^+ + 3H_2O + 2Zn^{2+}$
D. $8Zn + NO_3^- + 20H^+ \rightarrow NH_8^+ + 6H_2O + 8Zn^{4+}$

40) TYPE: M   LEVEL: 1   TEXT REFERENCE: 21-4
ANSWER: D

A salt bridge is a U-tube container holding a concentrated solution of a(n):

A. weak base.   C. strong acid.
B. weak acid.   D. strong electrolyte.

41) TYPE: M   LEVEL: 1   TEXT REFERENCE: 21-4
ANSWER: A

Which of the following metals is the most easily oxidized?

A. K   C. Fe
B. Au   D. Al

Chapter 21 ELECTROCHEMISTRY

42) TYPE: M   LEVEL: 2   TEXT REFERENCE: 21-4
ANSWER: D

A metal that is easily oxidized is also:

A. easily reduced.   C. a weak reducing agent.
B. a weak oxidizing agent.   D. a strong reducing agent.

43) TYPE: M   LEVEL: 1   TEXT REFERENCE: 21-5
ANSWER: C

Voltage is used to measure which property of electricity?

A. amount of flow
B. rate flow
C. tendency to flow
D. temperature at which electrons will flow

44) TYPE: M   LEVEL: 1   TEXT REFERENCE: 21-5
ANSWER: B

Ten amperes is the same as:

A. 10 coulombs.
B. 10 coulombs/second.
C. 10 volts.
D. 1.01×10^{-4} mole of electrons.

45) TYPE: M   LEVEL: 1   TEXT REFERENCE: 21-5
ANSWER: A

Half-cell potentials are symbolized by:

A. E.   C. Hc.
B. HC.   D. P.

46) TYPE: M   LEVEL: 1   TEXT REFERENCE: 21-5
ANSWER: C

The hydrogen half-cell potential is:

A. 1.00 volts.   C. 0.00 volts.
B. 0.00 amperes.   D. 0.00 coulombs.

47) TYPE: M   LEVEL: 1   TEXT REFERENCE: 21-5
ANSWER: A

An atom that exhibits a greater tendency than hydrogen ions to accept electrons will have a half-cell potential that is:

A. positive.
B. negative.
C. less than zero.
D. less than the half-cell potential for hydrogen.

48) TYPE: M   LEVEL: 2   TEXT REFERENCE: 21-5
ANSWER: D

A positive cell potential indicates:

A. the reaction is at equilibrium.
B. the reaction will not proceed spontaneously.
C. the synthesis reaction is favored.
D. none of the above.

49) TYPE: M   LEVEL: 1   TEXT REFERENCE: 21-7
ANSWER: D

Which of the following is not an example of a dry cell?

A. Leclanche cell.   C. alkaline battery.
B. alkaline manganese cell.   D. lead storage battery.

50) TYPE: M   LEVEL: 2   TEXT REFERENCE: 21-7
ANSWER: C

The most efficient way to keep the sulfuric acid in a car battery from freezing is to:

A. add water to the battery.
B. dilute the electrolyte.
C. recharge the battery.
D. lower the concentration of the sulfuric acid.

51) TYPE: M   LEVEL: 1   TEXT REFERENCE: 21-7
ANSWER: C

Which of the following equations expresses the chemistry of the alkaline battery?

A. $Pb + SO_4^{2-} \rightarrow PbSO_4 + 2e^-$
B. $Zn \rightarrow ZnO$
C. $Zn + 2MnO_2 \rightarrow ZnO + Mn_2O_3$
D. $Zn + 2PbO_2 \rightarrow ZnO + Pb_2O_3$

Chapter 21   ELECTROCHEMISTRY

52) TYPE: M   LEVEL: 1   TEXT REFERENCE: 21-9
ANSWER: B

One by-product of the electrolysis of water is:

A. pure oxygen.   C. an electric current.
B. hydrogen sulfide gas.   D. sulfuric acid.

53) TYPE: M   LEVEL: 1   TEXT REFERENCE: 21-9
ANSWER: C

During the electrolysis of aluminum ore, what substance is produced
at the cathode?

A. aluminum oxide   C. aluminum metal
B. aluminum ion   D. cryolite

54) TYPE: M   LEVEL: 3   TEXT REFERENCE: 21-10
ANSWER: A

Which of the following methods would not be used to protect a piece
of iron from corrosion?

A. submerging it completely in water
B. putting grease on it
C. coating it with zinc
D. placing it in an airtight container

55) TYPE: M   LEVEL: 4   TEXT REFERENCE: LA
ANSWER: B

In a copper-zinc cell, the number of electrons lost by the zinc atoms
is:

A. equal to the number of electrons lost by the Cu ions.
B. equal to the number of electrons gained by the Cu ions.
C. more than the number of electrons gained by the Cu ions.
D. less than the number of electrons gained by the Cu ions.

56) TYPE: M   LEVEL: 4   TEXT REFERENCE: LA
ANSWER: A

The voltage produced by a copper-zinc cell is:

A. less than the voltage of a dry cell.
B. greater than the voltage of a dry cell.
C. equal to the voltage of a dry cell.
D. four times as great as the voltage of a dry cell.

57) TYPE: M   LEVEL: 4   TEXT REFERENCE: LA
ANSWER: C

In a copper-zinc cell, the mass lost by the zinc electrode is:

A. equal to the mass lost by the Cu electrode.
B. equal to the mass gained by the Cu electrode.
C. greater than the mass gained by the Cu electrode.
D. less than the mass gained by the Cu electrode.

58) TYPE: M   LEVEL: 4   TEXT REFERENCE: LA
ANSWER: B

What is the overall equation for the reaction in a zinc/copper cell?

A. $Zn(s) + Cu^{2-}(aq) \rightarrow Zn^{2-}(aq) + Cu(s)$
B. $Zn(s) + Cu^{2+}(aq) \rightarrow Zn^{2+}(aq) + Cu(s)$
C. $Zn(s) + Cu^{2+}(aq) \rightarrow ZnCu(s)$
D. $Zn(s) + Cu^{2-}(aq) \rightarrow ZnCu(s)$

59) TYPE: M   LEVEL: 4   TEXT REFERENCE: LB
ANSWER: A

What color precipitate is associated with the anodic regions of an oxidized nail?
A. blue   C. pink
B. gray   D. yellow

60) TYPE: M   LEVEL: 4   TEXT REFERENCE: LB
ANSWER: C

What color change would be most noticeable along a nail that has been bent ninety degrees, then oxidized?

A. pink   C. blue
B. yellow   D. gray

61) TYPE: M   LEVEL: 4   TEXT REFERENCE: LB
ANSWER: A

Contact with which of the following metal strips will decrease the formation of Fe_2O_3 on a nail?

A. Mg   C. Cu
B. neither Mg nor Cu   D. cannot tell

62) TYPE: M   LEVEL: 4   TEXT REFERENCE: LB
ANSWER: D

The purpose of a salt bridge is to:

A. prevent a flow of electrons.
B. measure electrical potential.
C. cause a buildup of charge.
D. insure electrical neutrality throughout a cell.

1) TYPE: T   LEVEL: 1   TEXT REFERENCE: 22-1
ANSWER: F

____ The reaction, $NiCl_2(aq) + K_2CO_3(aq) \rightarrow NiCO_3(s) + 2KCl(aq)$ produces the precipitate potasssium chloride.

2) TYPE: T   LEVEL: 2   TEXT REFERENCE: 22-2
ANSWER: T

____ A noticeably exothermic reaction can mean that an acid has been mixed with a base.

3) TYPE: T   LEVEL: 1   TEXT REFERENCE: 22-3
ANSWER: F

____ An indication of the presence of the ammonium ion is the greenish color produced by the addition of NaOH.

4) TYPE: T   LEVEL: 1   TEXT REFERENCE: 22-3
ANSWER: T

____ It is often helpful when trying to identify the compounds in a mixture to separate substances by means of precipitation.

5) TYPE: T   LEVEL: 2   TEXT REFERENCE: 22-4
ANSWER: T

____ Precipitation cannot be used to confirm the presence of K^+ because potassium salts are soluble.

6) TYPE: O   LEVEL: 1   TEXT REFERENCE: 22-1
ANSWER: reagent

A(n) _____ is a substance used to detect, measure or produce other substances.

7) TYPE: O   LEVEL: 1   TEXT REFERENCE: 22-4
ANSWER: flame

A test used to identify metal ions by their color when burned is called a(n) _____ test.

8) TYPE: O   LEVEL: 3   TEXT REFERENCE: 22-5
ANSWER: centrifuge

A(n) _____ rapidly spins a test tube, causing a dense precipite to settle at the bottom of the tube.

9) TYPE: M   LEVEL: 1   TEXT REFERENCE: 22-1
ANSWER: D

Which of the following is a macroscopic observation?

A. Heat is given off.   C. No reaction.
B. A precipitate forms.   D. all of the above.

10) TYPE: M   LEVEL: 1   TEXT REFERENCE: 22-4
ANSWER: A

If the result of a flame test is a scarlet colored flame, which
substance is indicated?

A. lithium   C. potassium
B. sodium   D. platinum

11) TYPE: O   LEVEL: 4   TEXT REFERENCE: LB
ANSWER: NO_3^-(aq)

The spectator ions in the reaction between HNO_3 and Li_2CO_3 are
Li^+(aq) and _____.

12) TYPE: O   LEVEL: 4   TEXT REFERENCE: LC
ANSWER: scarlet

The color of the lithium ion flame is _____.

13) TYPE: O   LEVEL: 4   TEXT REFERENCE: LC
ANSWER: violet

The color of the potassium flame is _____.

14) TYPE: O   LEVEL: 4   TEXT REFERENCE: LC
ANSWER: yellow

The color of the sodium ion flame is _____.

15) TYPE: O   LEVEL: 4   TEXT REFERENCE: LC
ANSWER: yellow

The color you would observe in a flame test of Na_2SO_4(aq)
solution is _____.

16) TYPE: M   LEVEL: 4   TEXT REFERENCE: LA
ANSWER: C

What is the equation for the decomposition reaction of carbonic acid?

A. $H_2CO_3 \rightarrow H_2O(l) + CO(g)$
B. $H_2CO_3 \rightarrow OH(g) + CO_2(g)$
C. $H_2CO_3 \rightarrow H_2O(l) + CO_2(g)$
D. $H_2CO_3 \rightarrow OH(g) + CO(g)$

17) TYPE: M   LEVEL: 4   TEXT REFERENCE: LA
ANSWER: D

What formula indicates which ions are present in a solution of hydrochloric acid?

A. $2HCl \rightarrow H_2 + Cl_2$
B. $HCl \rightarrow H_2 + Cl_2$
C. $HCl \rightarrow H^-(aq) + Cl^+(aq)$
D. $HCl \rightarrow H^+(aq) + Cl^-(aq)$

18) TYPE: M   LEVEL: 4   TEXT REFERENCE: LA
ANSWER: C

What is the precipitate that forms when $CuSO_4$ reacts with $Pb(NO_3)_2$?

A. Cu^+ C. $PbSO_4(s)$
B. Pb^{2+} D. $SO_4(s)$

19) TYPE: M   LEVEL: 4   TEXT REFERENCE: LA
ANSWER: D

Which are the spectator ions in the reaction between $CuSO_4$ and $Pb(NO_3)_2$?

A. $PbSO_4(s)$ and $Cu(NO_3)_2(s)$
B. $Cu^{2+}(aq)$
C. $NO_3^-(aq)$
D. both B and C

20) TYPE: M   LEVEL: 4   TEXT REFERENCE: LB
ANSWER: C

What is the left side of the ionic equation for the reaction between HCl and K_2CO_3?

A. $2H^+(aq) + 2Cl^-(aq) + K_2(aq) + CO_3^{2-}$
B. $2H^+(aq) + Cl^-(aq) + 2K^+(aq) + CO_3^{2-}$
C. $2H^+(aq) + 2Cl^-(aq) + 2K^+(aq) + CO_3^{2-}$
D. $H_2(aq) + 2Cl^-(aq) + 2K^+(aq) + CO_3^{2-}$

21) TYPE: M   LEVEL: 4   TEXT REFERENCE: LB
ANSWER: B

Which are the spectator ions in the reaction between HCl and Li_2CO_3?

A. $CO_3^-(aq)$ and $H^+(aq)$
B. $Li^+(aq)$ and $Cl^-(aq)$
C. $CO_3^-(aq)$ and $H^+(aq)$
D. $Li^-(aq)$ and $Cl^+(aq)$

22) TYPE: M   LEVEL: 4   TEXT REFERENCE: LB
ANSWER: D

Which of the following reactions does not have the same net ionic equation as the others?

A. NH_4I and Li_2CO_3
B. NH_4I and K_2CO_3
C. HNO_3 and Li_2CO_3
D. HNO_3 and KI

23) TYPE: M   LEVEL: 4   TEXT REFERENCE: LC
ANSWER: A

What color would you observe in a flame test of a $LiNO_3(aq)$ solution?

A. scarlet   C. yellow
B. violet   D. green

24) TYPE: M   LEVEL: 4   TEXT REFERENCE: LC
ANSWER: B

What color would you observe in a flame test of a $KNO_3(aq)$ solution?

A. scarlet   C. yellow
B. violet   D. green

25) TYPE: M   LEVEL: 4   TEXT REFERENCE: LC
ANSWER: C

If the flame test of a 0.5M solution resulted in a red flame, what color will most likely be observed in a flame test of a 2.0M solution of the same chemical?

A. a pink flame   C. a redder flame
B. the same red flame   D. a yellow flame

Chapter 23 ORGANIC CHEMISTRY

1) TYPE: T   LEVEL: 1   TEXT REFERENCE: 23-1
ANSWER: T

_____   Most hydrocarbons are nonpolar.

2) TYPE: T   LEVEL: 1   TEXT REFERENCE: 23-1
ANSWER: F

_____   Most hydrocarbons are easily dissolved in water.

3) TYPE: T   LEVEL: 1   TEXT REFERENCE: 23-2
ANSWER: T

_____   It is possible to synthesize organic chemicals in laboratories.

4) TYPE: T   LEVEL: 1   TEXT REFERENCE: 23-3
ANSWER: T

_____   Carbon atoms have four electrons available for bonding that can
        be shared in a maximum of four covalent bonds.

5) TYPE: T   LEVEL: 2   TEXT REFERENCE: 23-4
ANSWER: F

_____   Molecules made entirely of single carbon-carbon bonds are
        relatively unstable.

6) TYPE: T   LEVEL: 1   TEXT REFERENCE: 23-4
ANSWER: T

_____   Hydrocarbons containing at least one double or triple bond are
        referred to as unsaturated.

7) TYPE: T   LEVEL: 1   TEXT REFERENCE: 23-5
ANSWER: F

_____   Alkanes have relatively high boiling points.

8) TYPE: T   LEVEL: 1   TEXT REFERENCE: 23-5
ANSWER: T

_____   The alkanes are an example of a homologous series.

Chapter 23 ORGANIC CHEMISTRY

9) TYPE: T   LEVEL: 1   TEXT REFERENCE: 23-6
ANSWER: F

_____ When naming a compound, different branches on the carbon-chain are listed in numerical order.

10) TYPE: T   LEVEL: 1   TEXT REFERENCE: 23-7
ANSWER: T

_____ In general, alkenes are more reactive than the corresponding alkanes.

11) TYPE: T   LEVEL: 1   TEXT REFERENCE: 23-8
ANSWER: T

_____ Alkynes are very reactive.

12) TYPE: T   LEVEL: 1   TEXT REFERENCE: 23-9
ANSWER: F

_____ Unsaturated cyclic hydrocarbons are usually less reactive than their saturated counterparts.

13) TYPE: T   LEVEL: 3   TEXT REFERENCE: 23-11
ANSWER: T

_____ Petroleum is the primary source of organic compounds used in the chemical industry.

14) TYPE: T   LEVEL: 1   TEXT REFERENCE: 23-12
ANSWER: F

_____ The functional group is the least reactive part of a molecule.

15) TYPE: T   LEVEL: 2   TEXT REFERENCE: 23-13
ANSWER: F

_____ Addition reactions may be performed easily across the double bonds of aromatic compounds.

16) TYPE: O   LEVEL: 1   TEXT REFERENCE: 23-2
ANSWER: coal

Beginning millions of years ago, layers of buried plant material were pressed into hard beds of _____.

17) TYPE: 0   LEVEL: 1   TEXT REFERENCE: 23-2
ANSWER: destructive distillation

The process of heating coal in the absence of air and collecting the
products is called _____.

18) TYPE: 0   LEVEL: 1   TEXT REFERENCE: 23-4
ANSWER: hydrocarbons

Carbon compounds containing only carbon and hydrogen atoms are called
_____.

19) TYPE: 0   LEVEL: 1   TEXT REFERENCE: 23-4
ANSWER: backbone

The longest carbon chain in a hydrocarbon molecule is frequently
referred to as the carbon _____, or skeleton.

20) TYPE: 0   LEVEL: 1   TEXT REFERENCE: 23-4
ANSWER: unbranched

Hydrocarbons that contain a single linear chain of carbon atoms are
called straight-chain, or _____ hydrocarbons.

21) TYPE: 0   LEVEL: 1   TEXT REFERENCE: 23-4
ANSWER: branched

Complex hydrocarbons composed of several carbon chains that cross are
called _____ hydrocarbons.

22) TYPE: 0   LEVEL: 1   TEXT REFERENCE: 23-10
ANSWER: aromatic

Carbon rings characterized by an alternation of double and single
bonds are called _____.

23) TYPE: 0   LEVEL: 1   TEXT REFERENCE: 23-5
ANSWER: alkanes

Straight- or branched-chain compounds with a general formula of
C_nH_{2n+2} are called _____.

24) TYPE: 0   LEVEL: 1   TEXT REFERENCE: 23-5
ANSWER: homologous

A series of compounds whose members differ by the addition of the
same structural unit is called a(n) _____ series.

25) **TYPE:** O   **LEVEL:** 1   **TEXT REFERENCE:** 23-6
ANSWER: structural isomers

Compounds with the same chemical formula but different arrangements
of atoms are called _____.

26) **TYPE:** O   **LEVEL:** 1   **TEXT REFERENCE:** 23-7
ANSWER: cracking

A process known as _____ is used to produce organic
molecules containing double-bonded carbon atoms from petroleum.

27) **TYPE:** O   **LEVEL:** 1   **TEXT REFERENCE:** 23-7
ANSWER: alkene

Straight- or branched-chain hydrocarbons containing at least one
double carbon-carbon bond belong to the _____ series.

28) **TYPE:** O   **LEVEL:** 1   **TEXT REFERENCE:** 23-8
ANSWER: alkyne

Hydrocarbon compounds containing a triple carbon-carbon bond belong
to the _____ series.

29) **TYPE:** O   **LEVEL:** 1   **TEXT REFERENCE:** 23-9
ANSWER: cycloalkane

A saturated hydrocarbon in the form of a ring is called a(n)
_____.

30) **TYPE:** O   **LEVEL:** 1   **TEXT REFERENCE:** 23-10
ANSWER: delocalized

Electrons that are not associated with any one carbon atom in a
benzene ring are said to be _____.

31) **TYPE:** O   **LEVEL:** 1   **TEXT REFERENCE:** 23-12
ANSWER: hydroxyl

Alcohols contain the functional group known as the _____
group.

32) **TYPE:** O   **LEVEL:** 1   **TEXT REFERENCE:** 23-12
ANSWER: carbonyl

Aldehydes and ketones both contain the _____ functional
group.

33) **TYPE:** O   **LEVEL:** 1   **TEXT REFERENCE:** 23-15
ANSWER: monomers

The basic repeating units found within complex molecular chains are called _____.

34) **TYPE:** O   **LEVEL:** 1   **TEXT REFERENCE:** 23-15
ANSWER: addition

The reaction that involves the bonding of monomers without the elimination of atoms is _____ polymerization.

35) **TYPE:** O   **LEVEL:** 1   **TEXT REFERENCE:** 23-15
ANSWER: peptide

The bond that joins two amino acids linked by an amide is called a(n) _____ bond.

36) **TYPE:** M   **LEVEL:** 2   **TEXT REFERENCE:** 23-2
ANSWER: D

Which of the following is a carbon-based molecule?

A. protein   C. sugar
B. wax   D. all of the above

37) **TYPE:** M   **LEVEL:** 1   **TEXT REFERENCE:** 23-4
ANSWER: B

When a structural diagram of a hydrocarbon is made, often the atoms not shown:

A. are carbon atoms.
B. are hydrogen atoms.
C. compose the carbon backbone.
D. are derivatives of the hydrocarbon.

38) **TYPE:** M   **LEVEL:** 1   **TEXT REFERENCE:** 23-5
ANSWER: A

The boiling points of the alkanes:

A. increase with increasing numbers of atoms.
B. decrease with increasing numbers of atoms.
C. increase with decreasing numbers of atoms.
D. are all equal.

39) TYPE: M   LEVEL: 1   TEXT REFERENCE: 23-5
ANSWER: D

Which of the following is the general formula for an alkane?

A. C_nH_n.   C. C_2H_n.
B. C_2H_6.   D. C_nH_{2n+2}.

40) TYPE: M   LEVEL: 2   TEXT REFERENCE: 23-5
ANSWER: C

The formula for the eight-carbon alkane compound is:

A. C_8H_8.   C. C_8H_{18}.
B. C_2H_8.   D. C_8H_{16}.

41) TYPE: M   LEVEL: 1   TEXT REFERENCE: 23-5
ANSWER: C

Four gases that may have played an important role in the evolution of
life are:

A. methane, butane, carbon dioxide, and oxygen.
B. methene, carbon dioxide, carbon monoxide, and oxygen.
C. methane, carbon dioxide, carbon monoxide, and hydrogen.
D. methene, carbon dioxide, carbon monoxide, and hydrogen.

42) TYPE: M   LEVEL: 2   TEXT REFERENCE: 23-5
ANSWER: B

Which of the following molecules would be expected to have the
highest melting point?

A. C_2H_6 C. C_8H_{18}
B. $C_{18}H_{38}$ D. they are the same.

43) TYPE: M   LEVEL: 2   TEXT REFERENCE: 23-6
ANSWER: C

An unbranched alkane containing eight carbon atoms is named:

A. 8-methane.   C. octane.
B. octide.   D. methyloctane.

44) TYPE: M   LEVEL: 2   TEXT REFERENCE: 23-7
ANSWER: A

Alkenes are generally more reactive than:

A. alkanes.   C. cycloalkynes.
B. alkynes.   D. all of the above.

45) TYPE: M   LEVEL: 2   TEXT REFERENCE: 23-9
ANSWER: D

A five-carbon cyclopentane would have the formula:

A. C_5H_5.
B. C_5H_{12}.
C. C_5H_9.
D. C_5H_{10}.

46) TYPE: M   LEVEL: 2   TEXT REFERENCE: 23-10
ANSWER: C

The carbon-carbon bond length in benzene is:

A. longer than a double
   bond.
B. shorter than a single
   bond.
C. both A and B.

D. neither A nor B.

47) TYPE: M   LEVEL: 2   TEXT REFERENCE: 23-10
ANSWER: B

The electrons are delocalized in which of the following molecules?

A. ethane.
B. benzene.
C. ethene.
D. both B and C

48) TYPE: M   LEVEL: 2   TEXT REFERENCE: 23-12
ANSWER: D

The molecule CH_3COCH_3 is a(n):

A. alcohol.
B. organic acid.
C. ether.
D. ketone.

49) TYPE: M   LEVEL: 2   TEXT REFERENCE: 23-12
ANSWER: A

The molecule hexanol contains which functional group(s)?

A. hydroxyl
B. carboxyl
C. carbonyl
D. hydroxyl and carbonyl

50) TYPE: M   LEVEL: 2   TEXT REFERENCE: 23-12
ANSWER: A

The addition of a hydroxyl group to a methyl (parent) group results
in a molecule named:

A. methanol.
B. methanoic acid.
C. methanone.
D. methanal.

51) **TYPE:** M **LEVEL:** 2 **TEXT REFERENCE:** 23-13
ANSWER: C

What type of reaction is represented by the equation
$$CH_4 + F_2 \rightarrow CH_3F + HF?$$

A. addition
B. oxidation

C. substitution
D. reduction

52) **TYPE:** M **LEVEL:** 2 **TEXT REFERENCE:** 23-14
ANSWER: B

What type of reaction is represented by the equation
$$CH_4 + 2O_2 \rightarrow CO_2 + 2H_2O ?$$

A. addition
B. oxidation

C. substitution
D. reduction

53) **TYPE:** M **LEVEL:** 4 **TEXT REFERENCE:** LA
ANSWER: B

How many structural isomers are possible for the alkane butane?

A. one
B. two

C. three
D. four

54) **TYPE:** M **LEVEL:** 4 **TEXT REFERENCE:** LA
ANSWER: A

How many structural isomers are possible for the alkane propane?

A. one
B. two

C. three
D. four

55) **TYPE:** M **LEVEL:** 4 **TEXT REFERENCE:** LA
ANSWER: C

How many structural isomers are possible for the alkane pentane?

A. one
B. two

C. three
D. four

56) **TYPE:** M   **LEVEL:** 4   **TEXT REFERENCE:** LA
ANSWER: A

An example of a pair of functional isomers is:

A. ethanol and dimethyl   C. butane and 2-methylpropane.
   ether.
B. 2-pentanol and   D. none of the above.
   3-pentanol.

57) **TYPE:** M   **LEVEL:** 4   **TEXT REFERENCE:** LB
ANSWER: C

The ester ethyl acetate is formed from acetic acid and:

A. ethane.   C. ethanol.
B. ethanoic acid.   D. methanol.

58) **TYPE:** M   **LEVEL:** 4   **TEXT REFERENCE:** LB
ANSWER: B

What is the name of the ester formed by ethanol and benzoic acid?

A. benzyl ethanate   C. ethanol benzate
B. ethyl benzoate   D. benzanol

59) **TYPE:** M   **LEVEL:** 4   **TEXT REFERENCE:** LB
ANSWER: D

What combination of alcohol and acid will form the ester octyl
benzoate?

A. benzanol and octanic acid
B. benzene and octanic acid
C. octane and benzoic acid
D. octanol and benzoic acid

60) **TYPE:** M   **LEVEL:** 4   **TEXT REFERENCE:** LB
ANSWER: B

The synthesis of an ester must be done:

A. in the presence of a strong base.
B. in the presence of a strong acid.
C. in a neutral solution.
D. either A or B.

1) TYPE: T   LEVEL: 1   TEXT REFERENCE: 24-1
ANSWER: T

_____   Cellulose is a carbohydrate.

2) TYPE: T   LEVEL: 2   TEXT REFERENCE: 24-1
ANSWER: T

_____   Glucose has the formula $C_6H_{12}O_6$.

3) TYPE: T   LEVEL: 1   TEXT REFERENCE: 24-1
ANSWER: F

_____   Starch is a disaccharide.

4) TYPE: T   LEVEL: 2   TEXT REFERENCE: 24-2
ANSWER: F

_____   If a fatty acid contains one carbon-carbon double bond and as
        many hydrogen atoms as possible on other carbon atoms, the fatty
        acid is saturated.

5) TYPE: T   LEVEL: 1   TEXT REFERENCE: 24-2
ANSWER: T

_____   Cholesterol is a steroid.

6) TYPE: T   LEVEL: 2   TEXT REFERENCE: 24-2
ANSWER: F

_____   Saturated fatty acids have a lower melting point than
        polyunsaturated fatty acids.

7) TYPE: T   LEVEL: 1   TEXT REFERENCE: 24-3
ANSWER: F

_____   A protein molecule is built by linking the amino group of one
        amino acid to the side chain of another amino acid.

8) TYPE: T   LEVEL: 1   TEXT REFERENCE: 24-3
ANSWER: T

_____   Hydrogen bonding between atoms of a protein increases its
        stability.

9) TYPE: T   LEVEL: 1   TEXT REFERENCE: 24-4
ANSWER: F

_____   A nucleotide is made of a phosphate group linked to a protein.

10) TYPE: T   LEVEL: 1   TEXT REFERENCE: 24-5
ANSWER: F

_____   Hormones made from strings of amino acids are steroids.

11) TYPE: T   LEVEL: 1   TEXT REFERENCE: 24-5
ANSWER: T

_____   Enkephalins are peptide hormones.

12) TYPE: T   LEVEL: 1   TEXT REFERENCE: 24-6
ANSWER: T

_____   All three stages in the action of an enzyme are reversible.

13) TYPE: T   LEVEL: 1   TEXT REFERENCE: 24-6
ANSWER: T

_____   Enzymes speed up biochemical reactions by lowering the energy
        needed to start the reactions.

14) TYPE: T   LEVEL: 1   TEXT REFERENCE: 24-7
ANSWER: F

_____   Vitamins are nonprotein, inorganic materials.

15) TYPE: T   LEVEL: 1   TEXT REFERENCE: 24-7
ANSWER: F

_____   Your body can manufacture all the vitamins and minerals
        necessary to function properly, but it cannot make all the
        enzymes it needs.

16) TYPE: O   LEVEL: 1   TEXT REFERENCE: 24-1
ANSWER: CH_2O

Carbohydrates have an empirical formula of _____.

17) TYPE: O   LEVEL: 1   TEXT REFERENCE: 24-1
ANSWER: monosaccharides

The simplest carbohydrates are the _____.

18) TYPE: O   LEVEL: 2   TEXT REFERENCE: 24-1
ANSWER: $C_{12}H_{22}O_{11}$

The formula for table sugar is _____.

19) TYPE: O   LEVEL: 1   TEXT REFERENCE: 24-2
ANSWER: lipids

Fats and oils belong to the class of biomolecules known as
_____.

20) TYPE: O   LEVEL: 1   TEXT REFERENCE: 24-2
ANSWER: polyunsaturated

A fatty acid that has two or more double bonds is called
_____.

21) TYPE: O   LEVEL: 1   TEXT REFERENCE: 24-2
ANSWER: steroids

Lipids that have a four-ring carbon skeleton are called
_____.

22) TYPE: O   LEVEL: 1   TEXT REFERENCE: 24-3
ANSWER: amino acids

Protein molecules are polymers made from smaller molecules known as
_____.

23) TYPE: O   LEVEL: 1   TEXT REFERENCE: 24-3
ANSWER: polypeptide

A protein chain is referred to as a(n) _____.

24) TYPE: O   LEVEL: 1   TEXT REFERENCE: 24-3
ANSWER: denatured

A protein whose three-dimensional structure has fallen apart is said
to be _____.

25) TYPE: O   LEVEL: 1   TEXT REFERENCE: 24-3
ANSWER: active site

Globular proteins usually include an area of specific shape called
the _____.

26) **TYPE:** O   **LEVEL:** 1   **TEXT REFERENCE:** 24-4
ANSWER: nucleotides

Nucleic acids are long-chain polymers made up of repeating units called _____.

27) **TYPE:** O   **LEVEL:** 1   **TEXT REFERENCE:** 24-4
ANSWER: ATP

_____ is a single nucleotide with three phosphate groups attached.

28) **TYPE:** O   **LEVEL:** 1   **TEXT REFERENCE:** 24-4
ANSWER: gene

A section of DNA that codes for a protein is called a(n) _____.

29) **TYPE:** O   **LEVEL:** 1   **TEXT REFERENCE:** 24-5
ANSWER: neurotransmitter

To send a message, the nerve cell releases a chemical called a(n) _____.

30) **TYPE:** O   **LEVEL:** 1   **TEXT REFERENCE:** 24-5
ANSWER: hormones

The glands of the endocrine system release chemicals called _____ that act on cells or organs.

31) **TYPE:** O   **LEVEL:** 1   **TEXT REFERENCE:** 24-6
ANSWER: enzymes

Biological catalysts that affect the rate at which reactions occur are called _____.

32) **TYPE:** O   **LEVEL:** 1   **TEXT REFERENCE:** 24-6
ANSWER: substrate

An enzyme binds to and acts on a _____.

33) **TYPE:** O   **LEVEL:** 1   **TEXT REFERENCE:** 24-7
ANSWER: coenzyme

A(n) _____ binds to a specific site on a protein molecule and provides chemical functions that an enzyme alone cannot provide.

34) TYPE: O   LEVEL: 1   TEXT REFERENCE: 24-8
ANSWER: cloning

The laboratory process that makes copies of a particular DNA sequence
is called _____.

35) TYPE: M   LEVEL: 2   TEXT REFERENCE: 24-1
ANSWER: A

What is the empirical formula for fructose?

A. CH_2O C. $C_{12}H_{22}O_{11}$
B. $C_6H_{12}O_6$ D. $C_2H_4O_2$

36) TYPE: M   LEVEL: 2   TEXT REFERENCE: 24-1
ANSWER: A

Glucose is a:

A. monosaccharide.   C. polysaccharide.
B. disaccharide.   D. lipid.

37) TYPE: M   LEVEL: 1   TEXT REFERENCE: 24-2
ANSWER: A

Long, staight chains of carbon atoms with a carboxyl group at one end
are called:

A. fatty acids.   C. amino acids.
B. steroids.   D. triglycerides.

38) TYPE: M   LEVEL: 1   TEXT REFERENCE: 24-2
ANSWER: B

Most animal fats are:

A. polyunsaturated.   C. unsaturated.
B. saturated.   D. polysaccharides.

39) TYPE: M   LEVEL: 2   TEXT REFERENCE: 24-2
ANSWER: B

If the carbons of a fatty acid each have as many hydrogen atoms as
possible and no double bonds, the fatty acid is:

A. polyunsaturated.   C. unsaturated.
B. saturated.   D. denatured.

40) TYPE: M   LEVEL: 2   TEXT REFERENCE: 24-2
ANSWER: A

Vegetable oils are liquid at room temperature because they are:

A. polyunsaturated.   C. saturated.
B. unsaturated.   D. denatured.

41) TYPE: M   LEVEL: 1   TEXT REFERENCE: 24-2
ANSWER: D

Steroids include:

A. lipids, proteins, and sex hormones.
B. lipids, cortisone, and sex hormones.
C. some vitamins, cortisone, and proteins.
D. some vitamins, cortisone, and sex hormones.

42) TYPE: M   LEVEL: 1   TEXT REFERENCE: 24-3
ANSWER: A

A protein molecule is made by linking the amino group of one amino
acid to the:

A. carboxyl group of   C. side chain of another.
   another.
B. amine group of another.   D. carbonyl group of another.

43) TYPE: M   LEVEL: 2   TEXT REFERENCE: 24-3
ANSWER: C

In a protein of 75 amino acids, how many possible sequences of amino
acids are there?

A. 75   C. 20^{75}
B. 75^{20} D. 20×75

44) TYPE: M   LEVEL: 1   TEXT REFERENCE: 24-3
ANSWER: A

Cross-linking between sulfur atoms in two cysteine molecules can
form:

A. covalent, disulfide bonds.
B. covalent, trisulfide bonds.
C. hydrogen bonds.
D. peptide bonds.

45) TYPE: M   LEVEL: 1   TEXT REFERENCE: 24-4
ANSWER: C

A nucleotide is made of:

A. DNA.
B. RNA.
C. a phosphate group, a five-carbon sugar molecule, and one nitrogen
   base.
D. adenine, guanine, thymine, and cytosine.

46) TYPE: M   LEVEL: 1   TEXT REFERENCE: 24-4
ANSWER: C

The pyrimidines in RNA are:

A. adenine and guanine.
B. thymine and cytosine.
C. cytosine and uracil.
D. adenine, guanine, cytosine, and uracil.

47) TYPE: M   LEVEL: 2   TEXT REFERENCE: 24-4
ANSWER: B

If the sequence of bases on one DNA strand is AGGTCCAAA, the base
sequence on the complementary strand would be:

A. AGGTCCAAA.   C. UCCAGGUUU.
B. TCCAGGTTT.   D. CAAGTTCCC.

48) TYPE: M   LEVEL: 1   TEXT REFERENCE: 24-5
ANSWER: C

Peptide hormones:

A. are derived from cholesterol.
B. include the glutocorticoids.
C. are strings of amino acids.
D. both A and B.

49) TYPE: M   LEVEL: 2   TEXT REFERENCE: 24-6
ANSWER: A

An enzyme that is specific will act upon:

A. one substate.
B. an entire class of substrates.
C. cholesterol.
D. lipids.

50) TYPE: M   LEVEL: 1   TEXT REFERENCE: 24-7
ANSWER: C

What mineral is important for bone growth and maintenance?

A. potassium   C. calcium
B. zinc   D. iron

51) TYPE: M   LEVEL: 1   TEXT REFERENCE: 24-7
ANSWER: D

Scurvy is a disease caused by a deficiency of the water soluble
vitamin:

A. thiamine.   C. retinol.
B. folacin.   D. ascorbic acid.

52) TYPE: M   LEVEL: 4   TEXT REFERENCE: LA
ANSWER: B

What happens when iodine is added to a starch solution?

A. it turns red   C. it turns yellow
B. it turns blue   D. nothing

53) TYPE: M   LEVEL: 4   TEXT REFERENCE: LA
ANSWER: C

What does a negative Benedict's test indicate?

A. an absence of proteins
B. an absence of fats
C. an absence of monosaccharides
D. none of the above

54) TYPE: M   LEVEL: 4   TEXT REFERENCE: LA
ANSWER: C

What eventually happens to glucose molecules in the body?

A. oxidation into CO_2 and energy
B. oxidation into water and energy
C. oxidation into CO_2, H_2O, and energy
D. nothing

55) TYPE: M   LEVEL: 4   TEXT REFERENCE: LA
ANSWER: A

Hydrolysis consists of breaking bonds by:

A. the addition of water molecules.
B. the use of an electrical current.
C. the addition of iodine.
D. none of the above.

56) TYPE: M   LEVEL: 4   TEXT REFERENCE: LA
ANSWER: D

The enzyme that breaks down starch in the human body is:

A. hydrolase.   C. salivase.
B. fructase.   D. amylase.

57) TYPE: M   LEVEL: 4   TEXT REFERENCE: LA
ANSWER: A

If a decrease in temperature causes an enzyme to stop working, what
will cause it to regain its activity?

A. increase in temperature
B. the addition of a catalyst
C. further decrease in temperature
D. it will never regain its activity

58) TYPE: M   LEVEL: 4   TEXT REFERENCE: LA
ANSWER: C

If an enzyme normally operates at 25° C, an increase in temperature
to 200° C will probably:

A. make it work much faster.
B. make it work much slower.
C. stop it from working.
D. not affect it.

59) TYPE: M   LEVEL: 4   TEXT REFERENCE: LA
ANSWER: D

If a large increase in temperature causes a protein molecule to stop
working, what will cause it to regain its activity?

A. decrease in temperature
B. further increase in temperature
C. the addition of a catalyst
D. it will never regain its activity